AQUEDUCTS
AND VIADUCTS
OF BRITAIN

Victoria Owens

AMBERLEY

To Charles

First published 2019

Amberley Publishing
The Hill, Stroud
Gloucestershire, GL5 4EP

www.amberleybooks.com

British Library Cataloguing in Publication Data.
A catalogue record for this book is available from the British Library.

ISBN 978 1 4456 8380 5 (print)
ISBN 978 1 4456 8381 2 (ebook)

Typesetting and Origination by Amberley Publishing.
Printed in Great Britain.

Contents

Chapter 1   Pioneering British Navigable Aqueducts   4

Chapter 2   Aqueduct Ambitions   13

Chapter 3   Early Viaducts   24

Chapter 4   Progress   32

Chapter 5   Problems   40

Chapter 6   Timber and Iron   49

Chapter 7   Case Study: The Viaducts of the Settle–Carlisle Railway   60

Chapter 8   Pushing the Boundaries   74

Chapter 9   New Visions for a New Century   81

             Further Reading   91

             Index of Bridges and Engineers/Contractors   94

             Acknowledgments   96

Chapter 1

Pioneering British Navigable Aqueducts

Before Britain's commercial canal network developed, people tended to associate aqueducts with water supply. Dr Johnson's 1755 *Dictionary of the English Language* preserves this idea by defining the term as 'A conveyance made for carrying water from one place to another'. It does not readily call to mind the idea of a bridge by which boats could cross rivers and valleys.

Around the 1760s, the word's meaning began to shift and expand. Navigable aqueducts had been a feature of the continental canal system for centuries. In the 1450s, Italian engineer Bertola da Novate had contrived a navigable aqueduct to take the Martesana Canal across the River Adda, near Milan. In France, the seventeenth-century Canal du Midi – brainchild of taxman, entrepreneur and supplier of munitions to the Catalan army Paul-Pierre Riquet (1609–80) – crossed the rivers Répudre and Cesse, and an unnamed stream near the village of Jouarres le Vieux, on three aqueducts as it made its way from Toulouse to the Mediterranean port of Sète. Making the Grand Tour in the 1750s, young Francis Egerton, the 3rd Duke of Bridgewater, visited it, and from that time on his zest for inland navigation never waned. Having returned to England, he obtained an Act of Parliament authorising construction of a canal from his estates at Worsley into Salford. It promised, at a stroke, both to drain his mines and provide an economical means of transporting his coal to its likely market.

Once his agent, John Gilbert, had recruited mill-wright and engineer James Brindley (1716–72) to the venture, it grew more ambitious. Abandoning the Salford scheme, the Duke petitioned Parliament for leave to build into Manchester, which would mean that the Bridgewater Canal would need to cross the River Irwell. Rather than lock down on one side and up on the other, the Duke, Gilbert and Brindley preferred to bridge the gap. Parliament evidently found the implications of this idea rather baffling. Tradition maintains that in order to show a bemused committee what the crossing would look like, Brindley improvised a model by cutting up a Cheshire cheese. Whatever the circumstances, on 12 March 1760 the Duke's new Act of Parliament received Royal Assent and construction went ahead on what would become known as the Barton Aqueduct.

Vuë de l'Aqueduc du Duc de Bridgewater.
Par J. J. Rousseau.

J. J. Rousseau, *Vue de l'Aqueduc du Duc de Bridgewater*. Dating from *c.* 1772/3, the picture shows a vessel crossing Brindley's Barton Aqueduct. The hoist would probably have been used to transfer materials between canal boats and craft on the river navigation. The structure which occupies the southern arch may have been intended as storage space. (Courtesy of the Trustees of the British Museum)

Little first-hand information concerning the building phase survives, but in view of the audacity of the venture, it would be surprising if nothing went wrong. According to one story, an unnamed 'gentleman of eminence' decried the whole project, observing that although he had heard of castles in the air, he had never before seen the location where one was to be built. Another tale maintains that the aqueduct showed early signs of buckling because Brindley applied so much puddle – the wet clay lining that keeps the channel watertight – at the sides of one of the arches that its sheer weight exerted more force than the structure could sustain. What truth the narrative holds is hard to say, but it is easy to see how the error might have occurred.

Whatever challenges its construction presented, the Barton Aqueduct opened on 17 July 1761 and a Bridgewater Estates Accounts ledger for 1760–61 now in Chetham's Library notes 10 guineas 'Pd. Workmen to drink by his Grace's order when the water went over the Bridge.' Not only did an excited crowd of spectators watch as the first vessels crossed it, but soon the sight of Bridgewater Canal boats gliding across the three sturdy arches became a popular spectacle. Among the visitors to Worsley were Joseph Banks the naturalist, Arthur Young, the agricultural writer, King Christian VII of Denmark and Jean-Jacques Rousseau, who made a captivating sketch of the aqueduct as it appeared through the arches of the old Barton road bridge. It survived until the 1890s, when it was demolished to make way for the Manchester Ship Canal.

Many of Brindley's remaining aqueducts are low-level and unassuming, like the two-arch sandstone bridge on which the Staffordshire & Worcestershire Canal crosses the River Stour. Nevertheless, his high-level Lumb Brook Aqueduct near Warrington, which carries the Bridgewater Canal across both a road and a stream – the Lumb Brook flows under the road's surface through an arched culvert – gives some sense of his ingenuity and daring. He also designed a remarkable twelve-span structure to carry the Oxford Canal over a wide valley near Brinklow, in Warwickshire. While one arch at its northern end crosses the Smite Brook, the eleven 'dry arches' were intended for use as storage, stabling and workshop accommodation. Within sixty years of their completion, the Brinklow Arches underwent a drastic change. In 1828, at the behest of the Oxford Canal Company, Marc Brunel and Charles Vignoles undertook to re-model and straighten the waterway's winding course. Their improvements included widening the channel at Brinklow by dumping spoil in most of the old arches to convert them into an embankment and lengthening the arch through which the Smite Brook flows. All that remains to be seen of the original aqueduct is the crown of one arch, which is just visible through the encroaching brushwood.

When Brindley died in September 1772, the task of completing and expanding the canal system fell to his colleagues, assistants and relatives. In the course of finishing the Trent & Mersey Canal, for instance, his brother-in-law, Hugh Henshall (1734–1816), designed and oversaw the construction of the Dove Aqueduct near Burton. Completed in 1777, its plain appearance belies the skill of its conception. Located on a flood plain, it had to be able to withstand surges of surplus water; fortunately Henshall, as engineering strategist, was quick to grasp and work with the local conditions. Since limited clearance between the surface of the River Dove and the bottom of the canal channel ruled out any question of building high arches, the aqueduct is instead massively long and able to accommodate the flood waters in several small watercourses.

Thomas Dadford of Wolverhampton (*c.* 1730–1809) met Brindley through employment on the Staffordshire & Worcestershire Canal. Dadford worked initially as a carpenter; later he took charge of lock-building and would in time contract to build the basins at Stourport. His sons followed him in his profession and in 1794 John Dadford, the second eldest, became engineer to the Montgomeryshire Canal Company. There was an understanding that his brother, Thomas Junior, would assist him and share his remuneration, but this arrangement was not proof against family tension. In 1797, an arch of the aqueduct by which the canal crossed the River Vyrnwy, near Llanymynech, collapsed. John resigned soon after and departed for America, leaving Thomas Junior to summon his ageing father to help with re-building it.

Despite the elder Thomas Dadford's intervention, the Vyrnwy Aqueduct was never satisfactory, and by 1823 all of its arches had cracked. George Watson Buck, the Montgomeryshire Canal Company's engineer at the time, first tried removing and replacing the watertight clay puddle that lined the channel. Noticing how the haunches of each arch bulged under the stress of the operation, he soon changed tactics and opted

Sir Edward Leader Williams designed the Barton Swing Aqueduct to take Bridgewater Canal traffic over the ship canal, which was made by deepening and widening part of the Mersey and Irwell Navigation. Boats enter the iron trough to proceed along the Bridgewater Canal; the arm swings to make way for vessels on the ship canal. (SJ 766 975)

The two-arch aqueduct at Stourton, by which the Staffordshire & Worcestershire Canal travels over the Worcestershire Stour. (SO864 856).

Lumb Brook Aqueduct, near Warrington. The stream runs through the culvert below the arch which takes the Bridgewater Canal over the road. (SJ 622 860)

Above left: One of the arch springers at Lumb Brook bears the date 1770.

Above right: Little survives of the Brinklow Aqueduct today except for the Smite Brook crossing and the crown of one of the dry arches, seen here as it appeared in summer 2014. (SP 443 802)

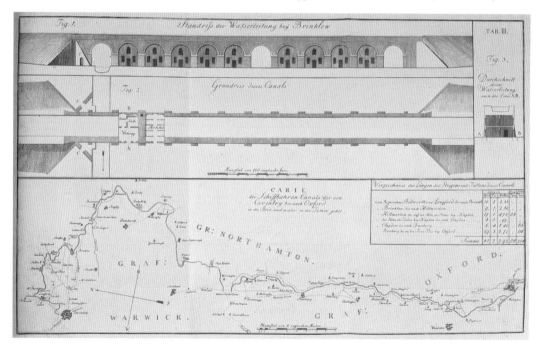

Hanoverian army officer and canal enthusiast Johann Ludwig Hogrefe visited England in the mid-1770s. This drawing of the Brinklow Aqueduct appears in his 1780 publication *Beschreibung der in England seit 1759 angelegten, und jetzt grostenheils vollendeten schiffbaren Kanale zur innem Gemeinschaft der vomehmsten Handelsstade ...* (Courtesy of the British Library and Bridgeman Images)

Hugh Henshall's twelve-arch aqueduct, which carries the Trent & Mersey Canal over the River Dove near Burton. (SK 268 269).

Built at the end of the eighteenth century, the bolts in the fabric of the River Vyrnwy Aqueduct on the Montgomery Canal and the supporting iron beams date from the 1820s. (SJ 254 197)

instead to reinforce the bridge by setting iron tie-rods through the arch spandrels. As a result, it bears many scars.

The condition of the younger Thomas Dadford's Teme and Rea aqueducts on the Leominster Canal is even worse. The canal was never profitable and when the engineer John Rennie inspected it in 1795 he was scathing about the quality of its construction. Even so, it enjoyed sixty years of unostentatious coal-carrying, before the Shrewsbury & Hereford Railway purchased it in 1858. The railway company drained the channel, sold off much of the land and ignored the aqueducts, which, without regular maintenance, began to decay.

In the Second World War, home defence forces denominated the River Teme as a stop line. Gripped by the fear of enemy invasion, the Home Guard decided to blow out the deck of Dadford's Teme Aqueduct above the middle arch. Apparently they did not appreciate that the clay puddle that lined the channel would absorb much of the force

The view along the towpath from the Vyrnwy Aqueduct. The Montgomery Canal is watered at this point, but not navigable.

The ruined aqueduct by which the Leominster Canal once crossed the River Teme. (SO 537 688)

of the blast. Having failed to demolish the bridge, they appealed to the regular army for assistance, but the army managed no better. At that point, the authorities brought in a shot-firer from Clee Hill Quarry. A skilled man, he knew precisely where to position the explosive so as to bring down the bridge.

The Rea Aqueduct's fate has been less dramatic, but equally melancholy. Once known as the Bridge of a Million Bricks, despite its increasing dilapidation Historic England gave it a Grade II listing and the towpath across it remained popular with walkers in the woodland near Mamble. In February 2013, the arch fractured and partially collapsed, leaving the aqueduct in what is probably a state of terminal decline. The loss of two fine bridges – one through wartime anxieties, the other from neglect – makes a sad testament.

The massive Kelvin Aqueduct on the Forth & Clyde Canal has enjoyed better fortune. Authorised in 1768, the canal benefitted from large-scale investment by Scots grandee Sir Lawrence Dundas and efficient direction of the early building phase by John Smeaton (1724–92). After this promising start, disagreements about the exact route led to delays and it was 1787 before work began on the River Kelvin crossing. By this time, Brindley protégé Robert Whitworth had succeeded Smeaton in the post of engineer in chief and, at 400 feet long and 700 feet high, his aqueduct would, as he expressed it, be something 'new and out of the common road of bridge building'. He estimated that it would cost in the region of £6,200 and while assessments differ as to how far it exceeded its budget, the aqueduct bankrupted contractor William Gibb who, avid to complete it on time, financed the final stages of its construction from his own pocket. Despite its cost, Glasgow viewed it as a stupendous status symbol and affirmation of the canal's importance. By way of marking the waterway's completion, on 28 July 1790 a party of city magistrates joined with the canal company proprietors to empty a ceremonious hogshead of Forth water into the Clyde.

The parlous condition of the aqueduct built in the 1790s to carry the Leominster Canal over the River Rea near Mamble. (SO 651 703)

The author's husband stands beside the aqueduct by which the Forth & Clyde Canal crosses the River Kelvin to give an idea of its size and scale. (NS 561 689)

In design terms, Whitworth's boldest stroke was to build each arch of the Kelvin Aqueduct with curved spandrels, softening what might otherwise have been a louring profile. Since this feature brought considerable force to bear on the bridge piers, Whitworth strengthened them with sizeable buttresses.

A view of the Kelvin Aqueduct at deck level, looking towards the Maryhill Locks.

Chapter 2

Aqueduct Ambitions

Amid the heated financial speculation and intense building which characterised late eighteenth-century canal mania, John Rennie (1761–1821) – he who had been so dismissive about the Leominster Canal – brought a new level of architectural flair to aqueduct design.

Completed in 1797, his most striking aqueduct takes the Lancaster Canal over the River Lune. Since a layer of clay puddle 3 feet thick lined the channel, it had to be as robust as it was ornate. Although the piers are hollow, rubble fills them, iron bars brace them from within and, by way of foundation, they rest upon piles made up of Russian timber. To make reliably hard-setting mortar, even in the submerged parts of the bridge fabric, Rennie imported volcanic pozzolana powder from Italy. Curving wing walls frame the five semi-circular arches while, at deck level, ornamental balustrades give grace to the parapet.

The Lancaster Canal was intended to link Kendal with the Wigan coalfields, and its proprietors anticipated that it would cross the River Ribble on a second stone aqueduct near Preston. In the event, Rennie's Lune Aqueduct depleted their funds to such an extent that they had no option but to bridge the Ribble with a wooden crossing and connect the canal's northern and southern sections by a tramway. Intended as a short-term measure, the canal company never raised enough capital to replace it. Apparently when Rennie discovered what they had spent on stone for his Lune Bridge, he expressed a wish that he had built in brick.

His Kennet & Avon Canal aqueducts at Dundas and Avoncliff are smaller but no less elegant. Built of the local stone, from the immense pilasters that flank Dundas's central arch to the ornamental balusters along its wing walls, the ornamentation of the whole structure rings with confidence. During construction of its sibling at Avoncliff, someone – perhaps an over-hasty contractor – appears to have removed the centring on which the middle arch was erected before the mortar had hardened and, as a result, it sags. Worse, the Murhill limestone from which it was built had a tendency to turn friable in frost, which may have exacerbated the flaw. Notwithstanding its blemished appearance, the aqueduct's long service is a tribute to Rennie's workmanship.

The autumn of 1794 was stormy and the weather wrought havoc with the nation's bridges. Among the casualties was the part-built stone aqueduct designed by engineer Josiah Clowes (1735–94) to carry the Shrewsbury Canal over the River Tern in

John Rennie's Lune Aqueduct from the north-west. The stone plaque carries a pledge, in Latin, of the canal's future success: QUAE DEERANT ADEUNT; SOCIANTUR DISSITA: MERCES FLUMINA CONVENIUNT ARTE DATURA NOVAS ['Things which were missing are present; things scattered, joined; rivers have come together by art to beget new wealth.'] The keystone of the central arch on its eastern side bears the dedication, 'To Public Prosperity'. Neither promise achieved fulfilment. (SD 484 639)

A fine balustrade flanks the Lancaster Canal as it crosses the Lune Aqueduct.

Rennie's Dundas Aqueduct on the Kennet & Avon Canal. The plaque on the eastern side commemorates Charles Dundas, Baron Amesbury, the canal company's first chairman. A similar plaque on the western side celebrates the achievements of John Thomas, Bristolian grocer-turned-engineer, who oversaw much of the canal's construction. (ST 784 625)

Rennie's Avoncliff Aqueduct, also on the Kennet & Avon Canal. A fine cornice crowns the stone courses of the spandrel area, which rise in alternate layer of ashlar and rusticated masonry. (ST 804 600)

Shropshire. Clowes died before he could direct its rebuilding, leaving the canal company with a pair of flood-ravaged abutments on either side of the Tern and a yawning gap in place of the crossing. To succeed him and repair the bridge, the company appointed Shropshire County Surveyor Thomas Telford (1757–1834), who was already overseeing the work in progress on the nearby Ellesmere Canal.

Rather than repair Clowes' stone structure, Telford replaced it, although he kept the abutments and flood arches. Having designed a cast-iron trough, he oversaw its fabrication at the Ketley Ironworks and installation at the site. Angular in outline, the sections that make up its walls are approximately wedge-shaped, like the voussoirs of a stone arch. Three piers support it, each consisting of two triple arms – one element is vertical; two set at an angle – which rise from the foundations with cross-pieces between to brace them. Completed in March 1796, it was not the first cast-iron aqueduct in the world – Benjamin Outram's iron Holmes Aqueduct on the Derby Canal opened a month earlier – but, unlike Outram's bridge, it did not leak. It was also considerably larger.

Even before the Shrewsbury Canal waters crossed the Longdon aqueduct, both Telford and Jessop had opted to use iron for the significantly larger high-level bridge by which the Ellesmere Canal would cross the Vale of Dee. On 25 July 1795, Richard Myddelton of Chirk Castle laid the first stone of the first pier of what would become known as the Pontcyssyllte Aqueduct – Telford's 'stream in the sky'. There were to be eighteen masonry piers with cast-iron arches between them, each made up of four cast-iron ribs. The task of ensuring that the discrete parts should fit together demanded the highest levels of precision and in 1802 Shrewsbury ironmaster William Hazledine – nicknamed 'Merlin' by Telford in tribute to his skill – tendered successfully for the contract to cast and erect the trough sections and high-level spans. Soon the site became a magnet for engineering-minded tourists, who drew up in their carriages outside resident engineer Matthew Davidson's cottage – now the Telford Inn – to view the ongoing work. Once the iron ribs were securely in place, the trough was bolted into position above them – its cast-iron plates, Longdon-wise, in the pattern of voussoirs.

The Longdon-on-Tern Aqueduct. Thomas Telford's innovative cast-iron aqueduct on the Shrewsbury Canal springs from Josiah Clowes' crumbling brickwork and masonry. (SJ 617 156)

The iron piers that support Telford's trough.

Towing boats across the Longdon-on-Tern Aqueduct must have been difficult, since the trough (seen here) is too narrow to allow the displaced water to escape around them.

Above left: Dating from *c.* 1800, Benjamin Outram's Stakes Aqueduct in Stalybridge is the world's oldest surviving navigable iron aqueduct. Taking the Huddersfield Narrow Canal over the River Tame, a stone bridge beside it carries the towpath. It may give some idea of the character of Outram's pioneering Holmes Aqueduct of 1795, which no longer survives. (SJ 954 9823)

Above right: At 1,007 feet (307 metres) long and 126 feet (38 metres) above the surface level of the River Dee, Pontcysyllte is Britain's longest and highest aqueduct. (Heather Freeman) (SJ 270 419)

The aqueduct opened on 26 November 1805 with a procession of boats bearing members of the canal committee, the engineering team and a band across it, high above the Vale of Llangollen. One vessel sported a banner proclaiming 'Success to the Iron Trade of Great Britain' and two barges went across empty, ready to be filled with Ruabon coal. Throughout the aqueduct's construction, there had been only one fatality, the luckless man's death resulting, Telford drily observed, 'from carelessness on his part'.

The advantages that iron offered in terms of economy, lightness and strength of aqueduct construction were too obvious for canal companies to ignore. When William Jessop's stone aqueduct on the Grand Union Canal at Cosgrove failed in 1808, Grand Union engineer Benjamin Bevan replaced it with the 'Iron Trunk', which opened in 1811. Since the Grand Union was a broad canal, to resist the extra loading from the sheer weight of water – and mindful, no doubt, of the fate of Jessop's bridge – Bevan introduced arched bracing beneath the trough floor. Around the same time, the Stratford -upon-Avon Canal Company employed Birmingham engineer William Whitmore (*c.* 1748–1816) to design and erect two (relatively) economical cast-iron trough

A view along the Llangollen Canal as it crosses the Pontcyssyllte Aqueduct. Here, cantilevers support a towpath above the water's surface, which avoids any recurrence of Longdon's water displacement problem.

Benjamin Bevan's 'Iron Trunk' on the Grand Junction Canal at Cosgrove. (SP 800 417)

aqueducts at Wootton Wawen and Edstone. The Wootton Wawen Aqueduct, which crosses the present A3400 – it was the old route from Winchester to Manchester through the Midlands – consists of a cast-iron trough supported on brick piers and abutments.

Whitmore's larger Edstone Aqueduct crosses a broad valley. Assembled from prefabricated cast-iron panels, their flanged sides bolted together, the trough rests on wrought iron trusses which surmount brick-built piers. Completed in 1816, it remains the longest aqueduct in England. In 1956, Warwickshire County Council, who owned the Stratford-upon-Avon Canal at the time, applied for a warrant of abandonment. Appalled local enthusiasts quickly formed a Protection Committee. Two of its members obtained a licence, borrowed a canoe and, travelling at weekends, traversed the canal's entire length by stages. Since their journeys demonstrated that it was still in use, the application to abandon it failed. The achievement lives on in local memory, and in March 2017 a band of canoeists recreated the original trip, paddling over the Edstone Aqueduct on their way. A small iron aqueduct carries the canal over a stream in the

The unassuming iron aqueduct by which the Stratford-on-Avon Canal crosses the present A3400 at Wootton Wawen. (SP 158 629)

Somewhat smaller than Pontcyssyllte, the Edstone Aqueduct is still impressive. It crosses railway tracks, a stream, a minor road and some low-lying pastureland. (SP 162 609)

nearby hamlet of Yarningale. Although it resembles Whitmore's workmanship, it is actually a product of the Horseley Iron Company. Dating from 1834, it replaced a timber bridge that collapsed in floods.

Though iron was useful, not everyone found it attractive. Resourceful Somerset engineer James Green, known as the builder of some ingenious boat-lifts, also designed lightweight iron aqueducts for use on the Grand Western Canal, which he contrived to install so as to avoid affronting the sensibilities of local grandees, the Sanford family. At first sight – particularly from a distance – Green's Tone Aqueduct of 1830 resembles a masonry bridge. It is in fact an iron trough set within a supporting frame and flanked by two stone arches, which largely conceal it. Green developed a rather more ambitious design for the aqueduct that crosses the carriage drive of Nynehead Court, the Sanfords' home. Presenting the appearance of a rather ornamental stone bridge, complete with compact pilasters, it is only when standing beneath the arch, or following the line of the canal where it crosses the deck, that the iron trough becomes visible.

Yarningale Aqueduct, located by an attractive lock on the Stratford-upon-Avon Canal. (SP 184 664)

James Green concealed the iron element of the aqueduct by which the Grand Western Canal crossed the River Tone within two masonry arches. The aqueduct is no longer navigable. (ST 146 223)

Even Thomas Telford, who clearly liked iron, chose on occasion to exploit its decorative potential to hide the more functional elements of his bridges. The iron tracery that decorates the small aqueduct by which he conveyed the modest Engine Arm feeder over his New Main Line to the adjacent Old Main Line of the Birmingham Canal is a florid exercise in BCN Gothic. The trough through which the feeder flows lurks behind an arcade of pointed arches topped with trefoils, with a latticework arch to support it and fine stone abutments at either end.

By the late 1830s, when iron was in wide usage on the nation's waterways, father and son George and John Wignall Leather devised what was probably the world's first iron suspension aqueduct. Built at the Milton Ironworks in Elsecar, it conveys a canal – the Aire & Calder Navigation – over the River Calder at Stanley Ferry, near Wakefield. Iron hangers suspend a set of frames which support the iron trough through which the canal passes. An aqueduct of innovative design, the Leathers chose to hide its business elements behind a Doric-style colonnade of cast-iron pillars.

Nynehead Aqueduct, which is also on the Grand Western Canal, presents the outward appearance of a stone bridge over the Nynehead Court carriage drive. (ST 143 217)

Nynehead Aqueduct's iron trough as it appears from below the arch.

The immensely ornate ironwork of Thomas Telford's Engine Arm Aqueduct, *c.* 1820, on the Birmingham Canal Navigation. (SP 023 888)

Stanley Ferry Aqueduct, with its Grecian colonnade. The white railing in the background belongs to a modern concrete aqueduct built in 1981. (SE 355 230)

The New Junction Canal aqueduct crossing the River Don at Bramwith. (SE 613 114)

Dating from 1995, this picture shows the Don in spate. The guillotine gates have been lowered to prevent the river from overflowing the canal. (Christine Richardson)

Later generations were less fastidious. Dating from the early twentieth century, the Sheffield & South Yorkshire New Junction Canal – the last canal to be built in England for commercial purposes – crosses the River Don on the Bramwith Aqueduct. The bridge makes no concession to taste, but extends across the river, immense and unadorned, its vast guillotine gates rising high above the quiet fields. When the Don is in full spate, they are lowered to prevent it from overflowing the canal and swamping the surrounding country.

Chapter 3

Early Viaducts

Neither etymology nor engineering history follows a straight course. To signify a manmade channel and, by extension, a navigable bridge the English language borrowed a bona fide Latin word *aquaeductus* meaning a conduit, or more literally, a leading of water. The rather similar sounding 'viaduct,' by contrast, owes its coinage to landscape designer Humphry Repton (1752–1818). The lavish improvement schemes that Repton planned for his genteel clientele included ornamental walkways over declivities, and disguised dams across rivers, with water at different levels on either side. Thinking that the plain term 'bridge' gave an inadequate sense of the elegance of these features, he lit upon the Latin words *via* – a road – and *ducere* – to lead – and thrust them together. While a bridge signified nothing more to Repton than 'a road across such a chasm as cannot be passed without one', in his opinion a 'Via-duct' splendidly combined 'strength with grace' and 'use with beauty'.

If it seems surprising that the technical term for a multi-span piece of road or rail infrastructure should derive from a finicky gardener's neologism, the explanation probably lies in the fact that, like re-modelling parkland, planning a railway required the services of a surveyor. Having honed their measuring and theodolite skills in landscape design, early nineteenth-century surveyors often found employment with the new

A 'Via-Duct' that Humphry Repton designed to cross a stream in the grounds of Woburn Abbey, Bedfordshire. 'The manner of passing,' Repton wrote, 'does not require a common bridge, but rather a viaduct, to ornament the dam or mound of earth thrown across the valley.' (Humphry Repton, *Fragments on the Theory and Practice of Landscape Gardening, Including some Remarks on Grecian and Gothic Architecture* (London: 1816) (Courtesy of Bristol University Library, Special Collections)

railway companies. In these changing conditions, it would not be improbable for them to introduce and adapt the language of the one sphere to the other.

Even before the noun gained much footing in the language, 'viaducts' existed in all but name. There is a striking example near Cockburnspath in the Scottish Borders, where the four-arch Pease Bridge spans the deep Pease Gorge – a notorious ravine. Describing the place in 1547, William Patten, chronicler of Edward Seymour's advance against the Scots, complained: 'So steep be these banks on either side, and deep of the bottom, that who goeth straight down shall be in danger of tumbling: and the comer up sure of puffing and pain.'

When the gorge was bridged, much of the impetus for the scheme came from the army, who reckoned that the gully was impassable for artillery. Designed in the 1780s by architect-cum-engineer David Henderson, the present sandstone bridge rises high above Pease Dean. Strengthened and modified, it remains in regular use by present day traffic on the A1107. Another notable early viaduct took shape around 1800 in South Wales, where engineer John Hodgkinson (1773–1861) contrived a bridge of thirty-two arches to take the horse-drawn Sirhowy Tramroad over the Ebbw Valley at Risca. Known as Risca Long Bridge, Hodgkinson ensured that it was high enough to keep the tramway clear of floods, to which the Ebbw was prone, and it remained in use until the 1850s. At that time, the tramroad reconstituted itself as the Sirhowy Railway and adopted a new course, which made the Long Bridge redundant. Even

Pease Bridge in Pease Gorge. The spandrels are pierced in order to reduce pressure on the foundations. (NT 379 699)

Above left: With four immensely high arches, Pease Bridge rises approximately 130 feet (39 metres) above the Pease Burn. In the 1780s, when it was built, it was thought to be the highest bridge in the world.

Above right: The surviving abutment of Risca Long Bridge, beside the B4591. (ST 238 907)

then, it was not demolished until 1902 and a single abutment remains at what was once its eastern end.

Promoted and financed by William Bentinck, the 4th Duke of Portland, the Kilmarnock & Troon Railway received its Act of Incorporation in 1808 and William Jessop (1745–1814) became its engineer. Like the Surrey Iron Railway – another of Jessop's ventures – which had opened between Wandsworth and Croydon in 1803, it was conceived as a horse-drawn enterprise, intended to carry both freight and passengers. At Laigh Milton it crosses the River Irvine on what is thought to be the world's earliest surviving viaduct on a public railway.

In 1816 the Duke enterprisingly acquired a locomotive from George Stephenson with the intention that it should haul coal from the Kilmarnock pits to the docks at Troon. According to eyewitness John Kelso Hunter (1802–73), the spectators loved it. 'The ease and grace', remembered Hunter, 'by which the huge machine snorted along the line and the composed way in which it was brought to a standstill, the reversing, and plying to and fro, seemed to have produced a new state of mind in the audience, who clustered round, touched it, and enquired as to how it was acted on and guided.'

Unfortunately, the engine's weight (a modest 5 tons) and speed played havoc with Jessop's track and railway records reveal substantial payments to the Kilmarnock Foundry Company in respect of rail-replacement. When the Kilmarnock & Troon

Laigh Milton Viaduct. Without the remedial work of the 1990s, the distorted arch (second from the left in picture) might well have collapsed. (NS 382 369)

A plaque above the entrance to Troon Town Hall commemorates the 4th Duke of Portland's locomotive. (NS 345 255)

Railway passed into the hands of the more commercial Glasgow & South Western Railway in 1846, rather than maintain Jessop's Irvine crossing, they preferred to realign the track and build a new bridge. The original viaduct, having undergone extensive restoration in the 1990s, remains open to walkers.

The adventures of the Duke of Portland's locomotive offer some explanation of why the arrival of the railways heralded a new era of bridge building. After all, loading upon a canal aqueduct came first from the weight of the bridge itself (dead load), and second from the people and horses on the towpath (live load.) Boats did not exert any pressure upon the bridge supports as they crossed it, as the mass of water that they displaced was equal to their own. With railway bridges new factors came into play. The structure needed to resist the dynamic pressure exerted by a live load consisting of moving traffic – locomotives and trains – and the varying stresses, such as vibration, that they exerted on the fabric.

The world's first public railway to use steam locomotives on a regular basis opened between Stockton and Darlington in 1825, and Darlington's Skerne Viaduct, designed by architect Ignatius Bonomi of Durham, has the distinction of remaining in continual railway use ever since. While John Dobbin's painting *The Opening of the Stockton & Darlington Railway, 1825* may not be accurate in every detail – he painted the festivities fifty years after the event – it portrays both bridge and embankment as fitting comfortably along with the fields and meandering river, so as to create a confidence-inspiring impression of solidity and permanence. At the same time, the bridge, theatrical as a stage curtain, sets off the distant, diminutive locomotive and its long but unassuming train.

Less picturesque than the Skerne Viaduct, George Stephenson's Gaunless Bridge is more daring, and, if not precisely a viaduct, it is hard to believe that it did not contribute to future viaduct design. An iron bridge designed for use by wagons on a colliery branch line, it is a small, delicate looking structure. Within each span, a lenticular – that is, biconvex – wrought iron truss made up of two curved iron girders locks into vertical supports which rise to the timber deck. As a pioneering truss bridge, it demonstrates Stephenson's shrewd understanding of the forces in play: the upper member of each truss, like an arch, is in compression; the lower member, in tension, with the idea that the equal forces, operating in opposite directions, cancel one another out.

The Liverpool & Manchester Railway was more ambitious than the Stockton & Darlington concern, and confronted Stephenson with greater challenges. Not only did it encounter much opposition in the promotion phase, but Stephenson's plan to cross Chat Moss was also much ridiculed. Loudest among the naysayers was fellow engineer Francis Giles (1787–1847), who insisted that a railway could not be built over the Moss without

The Skerne Viaduct as it appears in John Dobbin's painting *The Opening of the Stockton & Darlington Railway, 1825*. (Courtesy of Head of Steam – Darlington Railway Museum)

The Skerne Viaduct,
photographed in July 2018.
(NZ 291155)

Built to take the West Shildon
branch of the Stockton &
Darlington Railway over the
River Gaunless at West Auckland,
George Stephenson's pioneering
cast-iron truss bridge now stands
outside the National Railway
Museum, York, YO26 4XJ.

A view along the deck of
Stephenson's Gaunless Bridge.

subsiding into it. It also had to cross the shallow valley through which both the Sankey Brook and the St Helen's Canal flowed. Concerned that the railway should give ample clearance to fully rigged Mersey Flats on the Sankey Brook Navigation, the navigation company insisted that any railway structure must be at least 60 feet above the water.

Not only did Stephenson build his line across Chat Moss, but his response to the navigation company's demands was to cross the Sankey Valley with all the ostentation that he and his colleagues – draughtsman Thomas Longridge Gooch and resident engineer William Allcard – could muster. A letter to his son Robert in 1827 reveals his initial plan. 'We have a most magnificent Bridge to build across the Sankey Valley near Newton,' he wrote eagerly, eschewing punctuation:

It will be 70 feet high so as to cross the masts of ships that navigate that canal I have drawen a plan on the gothick principal there will be 20 arches of 40 feet span it will be quite a novel[ty] in England as there will be a flat arch sprung between the centre of the tops of the gothick and so on it has a fine a pearance in the plans.

It is not known when the gothic element, together with the 'flat arch' disappeared, but the Sankey Viaduct's design clearly changed. In its finished form, the viaduct had nine arches, which are not conspicuously 'gothic'. In comparison with the Pontcysyllte Aqueduct, it may seem squat and bulky, but combined with the excitement of the

The Sankey Viaduct, built to cross the Sankey Brook and Canal near Warrington. When the Liverpool & Manchester Railway opened in 1830, Joseph Kirwan, who travelled over the viaduct behind the locomotive *Arrow*, saw horse-drawn vehicles thronging the lanes beneath it, while boats on the Sankey Canal paused to allow the crews to admire 'the gorgeous pageant passing far above their mast heads.' (Joseph Kirwan, *A Descriptive and Historical Account of the Liverpool and Manchester Railway*: Glasgow and London, 1831). (SJ 568 947)

introduction of locomotives, at the railway's opening it made a sensation. Straddling both the St Helen's Canal and the Sankey Brook, the eight splayed piers in louring yellow-grey sandstone give a defiant answer to the navigation company's demands. Curving wing-walls support and retain the approach embankments at either end.

Incidentally, risk-averse Francis Giles, who evinced such scorn for Stephenson's assault upon Chat Moss, went on to design some stupendously bold viaducts for the Newcastle & Carlisle Railway. Dating from 1831–33, Giles' Wetheral Viaduct crosses the River Eden on five arches of red sandstone with a footpath running along the deck beside the line. Its neighbour at Gelt, which opened in 1835, is smaller but no less striking. Both remain in railway use.

Looking up at the viaduct which Francis Giles designed to cross the River Gelt in Cumbria. (NY 532 573)

Built in the early 1830s, Wetheral Viaduct crosses the River Eden at a height of approximately 95 feet (29 metres). As the picture shows, its river piers have been strengthened. (NY 468 546)

Chapter 4

Progress

If railways originated in the north of England, London was quick to adopt them. In 1833, a promotional pamphlet came out entitled *The Advantage of Railways with Locomotive Engines, especially the London & Greenwich Railway or Viaduct*. Notwithstanding the anonymous author's apparent uncertainty about whether the 'Viaduct' was the new transport system or its architecture, the idea of an elevated track suited the London–Greenwich enterprise well; the line would run upon 878 arches in total, all the way along its 3.5-mile route between London Bridge and outlying Greenwich.

The scheme's engineer was George Thomas Landmann (1779–1854), an army officer and son of the Professor of Fortification and Artillery at the Royal Military Academy, Woolwich. Amid the densely populated streets of Bermondsey, the sheer number of crossings required precluded any question of building at ground level, while the planned route around Rotherhithe and Deptford crossed marshy ground through which streams ran from mire to mire. In these conditions, the experience of building bridges that Landmann had gained while serving with the Royal Engineers counted for much.

In economic terms, it was a demanding project. To overcome the poor foundation afforded by the peaty subsoil, Landmann set the piers of his viaducts in a layer of concrete. Although the measure worked moderately well, movement of the piers was a constant worry; indeed, shortly before the railway's opening in 1836, two arches collapsed and required rebuilding. Furthermore, the project required a vast quantity of materials, with the labourers laying about 100,000 bricks daily. In these conditions, the cost of bricks rose fast, particularly since the promise of the railway started a wave of building across south-east London. To raise additional revenue, the London & Greenwich Railway opened a trackside walkway from which, for a fee, spectators could observe the railway works in progress; they would later lease their arches to accommodate small businesses. Trains first ran on the line experimentally in 1835; after that it opened by stages, achieving the complete connection from London Bridge station to Greenwich in 1838.

Although Landmann oversaw the London & Greenwich Railway's construction, responsibility for recruiting labour and the actual work of building fell to the contractor Hugh McIntosh. Contractors had been around throughout the canal era, and McIntosh, who worked on London's East India Dock, was able and reliable, but in the early phases of the railway era their professional reputation was not good; they had a name

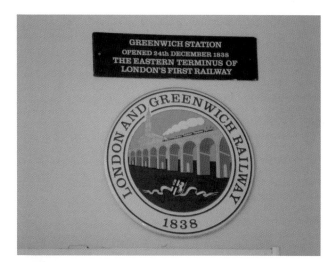

A plaque at Greenwich station commemorates the opening of the London & Greenwich Railway and illustrates its reliance on viaduct construction. (TQ 368 775)

Arches along the line of the former London and Greenwich Railway are leased to small businesses.

for making exorbitant charges while employing unskilled labourers and paying them a pittance. Furthermore, few of the early engineers issued written specifications of the work required and the standard to which it was to be executed, let alone itemising its costs; instead, the unspoken understanding was that they would give the contractor *ad hoc* orders during site visits and draw up costings on the hoof. It was hardly surprising then if contractors sought to take advantage of this lax approach to project management.

Engineer Joseph Locke demonstrated how the contracting system might be set on more regular footing when young contractor Thomas Brassey tendered to build a section of the Grand Junction Railway, which included a viaduct at Penkridge in Staffordshire. Its construction promised to be demanding since it required unusually deep foundations where it crossed the River Penk and, anticipating trouble, Brassey cautiously priced the work at the large sum of £26,000. Rather than dismiss his tender out of hand, Locke, who knew and respected him, suggested breaking the job down into discrete elements

The viaduct at Penkridge, which Thomas Brassey was contracted to build in the mid-1830s. (SJ 920 144)

and costing them on a precise rather than a speculative basis. By this method, it was possible to draw up a specification for building the viaduct at the modest sum of £6,000 and Brassey's tender, by which he undertook both to provide both men and materials, was accepted. Admittedly his labourers – hard-working, hard-drinking navvies who were not short of cash in hand – made themselves thoroughly unpopular with the Penkridge residents, but having opened in 1837, Brassey's viaduct remains in use.

The contract for constructing the significantly larger viaduct near Dutton in Cheshire which crosses the River Weaver and the Weaver Navigation went to McIntosh. Built of red sandstone, its twenty arches made it the longest viaduct on the Grand Junction Railway. Remarkably, in view of its size and scale, work on the Dutton Viaduct progressed both swiftly and safely; a banquet in December 1836 celebrated its completion in three years without any loss of life.

In 1834, the Great Western Railway Bill began what was to be a stormy passage through Parliament. Only at the second attempt did it become law, its success owing much to Lord Wharncliffe's adroit chairmanship of the committee charged with examining its clauses. In August 1835, the Act of Parliament authorising the line's construction received Royal Assent and the first contract to be let out went to Samuel Morton Peto and Thomas Grissell for the construction of a viaduct designed by Isambard Kingdom Brunel (1806–59) to cross the Brent Valley near Hanwell.

Appreciative of Lord Wharncliffe's deft handling of their Bill, the railway not only named the viaduct after him, but also set its gratitude in stone with a plaque on the south side bearing the Wharncliffe coat of arms and motto – *Avita Viret Honore* [he flourishes by ancestral honour]. With its eight distinctively shallow arches, the viaduct's size and style made an eloquent point about railway prestige. Further, to reduce weight on the foundations, the supporting piers are hollow and taper pylon-wise from base to a projecting cornice, which provided support for the centring round which the arches were built.

Incorporated in 1837, the London & Brighton Railway took a relatively direct route through the Sussex Downs. Not only did the line require expensive tunnelling, but it also needed to cross the wide Ouse Valley near Balcombe. Making a virtue of necessity, the

The 1836 Dutton Viaduct, near Acton in Cheshire. Now part of the West Coast Main Line, the route was electrified in the 1960s. (SJ 582 763)

A rather romantic depiction of the Dutton Viaduct by moonlight from Thomas Roscoe's travellers' guide, *The Book of the Grand Junction Railway*. (Courtesy of the Institution of Civil Engineers)

Although London has encroached around Brunel's Wharncliffe Viaduct, the Brent hay meadow, seen in the foreground of the photograph, is a reminder of the pastureland in which it was built. (TQ 149 803)

Lord Wharncliffe's arms on the fabric of the Wharncliffe Viaduct.

railway spent lavishly on the Balcombe Viaduct, which would serve as both an essential piece of infrastructure and an aesthetic trophy. Having commissioned architect David Mocatta (1806–82) to collaborate with engineer John Urpeth Rastrick (1780–1856) in its design, the railway sanctioned the purchase and import of some eleven million bricks from Holland for the bridge's construction, together with limestone from Caen for its decorative features (namely the parapets and pavilions). These expensive materials were shipped to the site along the River Ouse Navigation, which was evidently more serviceable for transport in the 1830s than it is at the present day.

Finished in 1841, the viaduct owes its finesse to the harmony of its separate elements. The piercings of the piers, for instance, resemble the shape of the arches, and the recurring half-circles lending a sense of integrity to the overall design. At the same time, the pale Normandy stone of the parapet balustrades and pavilions serves to frame the structure so that it stands out within the surrounding landscape. If it dented railway funds, the viaduct also bolstered local pride. At the time of its completion, the *Brighton Gazette*, condescending to a plucky little rival, published an account of George Watson Buck's viaduct in Stockport – twenty-seven arches to Balcombe's thirty-seven – which had opened the previous year.

When the Brighton journalist observed that the Stockport arches 'literally stride over that large town,' he portrayed it as a force of nature, heedless of anything in its path. The striding metaphor has an ambivalent quality that fits the Viaduct Age well. Both the Stockport viaduct and its twenty-three-arch sibling, which crosses the meadowland near Holmes Chapel, epitomise the inexorable aspect of railway growth. Built in plain red brick and boasting little decoration other than stone bands at the imposts and dentils below the parapet, each dominates and overshadows its surroundings. At the same time, both of them have the unassuming steadfastness of natural features, claiming their place within the landscape and lending it a measure of symmetry and grace. Besides, there is something intrinsically thrilling about a great bridge.

1850 saw the completion of Robert Stephenson's twenty-eight-arch masonry viaduct between Berwick and Tweedmouth – the largest bridge of its type in Britain. Known at the planning stage as the 'Tweed Viaduct', when Queen Victoria opened it the

February sun on the Balcombe Viaduct catches the contrast between the red-brown brickwork of the arches and the cream-coloured Caen stone used in the parapet and ornamental pavilions. (TQ 322 279)

The twenty-seven-arch Stockport Viaduct, designed by George Watson Buck. (SJ 891 902)

With twenty-three arches, the Holmes Chapel Viaduct, also designed by Buck, resembles Stockport in appearance, if not setting. (SJ 771677)

viaduct acquired the sobriquet 'The Last Act of the Union'. Nationalistic punning aside, Stephenson's bridge provided a crucial final link in the east coast route between London and Edinburgh, thereby saving passengers the trouble of a long detour inland to cross the Tweed. At the Queen's suggestion, it acquired the official, if misleading, name of the 'Royal Border Bridge'. Strictly speaking, the railway crosses the Anglo-Scots border 3 miles north of the Tweed at Marshall Meadows, but the 'Royal Border' appellation for the viaduct has a fine ring.

Around the same time that the Tweed Viaduct was under construction, Scots engineer John Miller (1805–83) built a number of bridges in the Borders and the West of Scotland that reveal viaduct design at its most dramatic. At fourteen arches, his Roxburgh Viaduct takes the Kelso branch line over the River Teviot. Impressive in itself, pleasingly and unusually its four river piers support an attractive wrought iron footbridge. Miller's Lugar Water Viaduct, built for the Glasgow & South Western Railway, stands in the mining town of Cumnock. As a necessary preliminary to building, Miller took considerable trouble to locate and fill the old workings round its site. Hidden now by

The Royal Border Bridge, seen early on a cloudless morning. (NT 992 532)

Roxburgh Viaduct. The iron footbridge appears to have been an integral part of its design. (NT 702 304)

the trees of Woodroad Park, it remains in regular rail use. Perhaps Miller's Ballochmyle Viaduct, which was built to take the Glasgow, Paisley, Kilmarnock & Ayr Railway over the River Ayr near Mauchline, offers the most memorable instance of his ability to enhance a striking location. Standing high above the river as it flows through a rocky cleft between high, wooded banks, it is composed of seven red sandstone arches with an immense central span of 181 feet. In 1848, when the viaduct opened – remarkably, it took only two years to build – it was the world's largest masonry arch. If the single span of Chester's Grosvenor Bridge was 19 feet longer, it had nothing like Ballochmyle's height. To make the voussoirs, Miller brought in hard stone from Dundee – a feature which offsets the texture of the local stone used in the rest of the bridge and bears witness to his eye for the telling detail.

Lugar Viaduct, which engineer John Miller regarded as his finest achievement, seen through the trees of Woodhead Park, Cumnock. (NS 573 206 to NS 574 205).

The central arch of Miller's Ballochmyle Viaduct, which spans the River Ayr at a height of 164 feet (50 metres). (NS 508 253)

Chapter 5

Problems

Near Rugeley, the Trent & Mersey Canal abandons its relatively straight course to cross the Trent at a 90 degree angle on Brindley's aqueduct. Among boaters, the tight turn in the canal's course at the aqueduct's southern end is notorious. Had Brindley perfected the art of building skew bridges, it might have spared canal men and their horses much trouble. Since there was no question of locomotives executing sharp turns, with the growth of the rail network the need to construct arch bridges that crossed roads, rivers and other obstacles at an angle other than 90 degrees became an absolute necessity.

As an example of a long bridge which includes some skew element, Alfred Stanistreet Jee's twenty-three-arch Saddleworth Viaduct, completed in 1849, crosses two roads and the Huddersfield Narrow Canal. Flat pilasters flank the sides of the three skew arches, which are recognisable from the distinctive spiral courses of stone in the vault. The 1851 Alston Arches, also known as the Haltwhistle Viaduct, takes the Alston Branch of the Newcastle & Carlisle Railway over the South Tyne on six arches, four of which are skewed.

Eighteenth-century engineer William Chapman evolved a formula for planning skew arches – their construction presented a major challenge to the masons who had to cut and lay the stone – which started from the premise of envisaging the arch as a series of slices.

Completed in 1849, the Saddleworth Viaduct, designed by Alfred Stanistreet Jee for the LNWR, crosses two roads and the Huddersfield Narrow Canal – shown here – at oblique angles. (SD 995 063)

The skew arch by which the Saddleworth Viaduct makes the canal crossing.

The Alston Arches, or Haltwhistle Viaduct, was completed in 1851. Four skew arches cross the South Tyne, with an additional semi-circular arch at either end. A delightful bridge, its designer, Sir George Barclay Bruce, may have contrived the small arches in the river piers as a means of reducing loading on the foundations. (NY 709 636)

If its curved underside – the soffit – were drawn out into a flat plane, it was possible to represent the slices as diagonal lines drawn on a parallelogram grid. These lines, he reasoned, could be transferred to the wooden centring used in the arch's construction as a guide for bricklayers and masons to follow in shaping the stone and setting it in place. How useful Chapman's formula was in practice is debateable. According to tradition, when Peebles-born architect Robert Murray and the Caledonian Railway's engineer George Cunningham planned the Neidpath Viaduct on the Caledonian Railway's Peebles–Symington branch, they illustrated the skew principle for the contractors by carving a working model from a turnip.

Besides the need to cross at oblique angles, viaducts that crossed rivers needed to withstand the effects of scour. For the six-arch viaduct built to take the Taff Vale Railway across the River Taff at Goitre Coed near Quaker's Yard, Brunel – the TVR's engineer – designed the piers in octagonal form. Having observed the flow of the Taff,

The Neidpath Viaduct's eight skew arches efficiently align the single-track railway with the Neidpath tunnel to its east. Slender, cruciform-pierced pilasters descending to the river piers and the ornamental cast-iron railings enhance its design. (NT 232 401)

The viaduct that I. K. Brunel designed in the 1830s for Goitre Coed was widened in the early 1860s by John Hawkshaw. Brunel's bridge faces upstream and is on the right-hand side in the photograph. (ST 087 965)

he reckoned that by aligning the sides of the octagon parallel to the axis of the river, it would be possible to bridge the river on the curve and mitigate the undermining effects of the current. Situated in a demanding location, with the Taff flowing fast through the steep-sided valley, the strategy enabled him to avoid adding what he termed 'the difficulty and expense of [making] the winding courses of a skew bridge' to the challenge of building the crossing.

Not every difficulty that attended viaduct building admitted a mathematical solution. When Robert Stephenson became engineer-in-chief to the London & Birmingham Railway, one of his early tasks was to design a viaduct to carry the railway over the Ouse near Wolverton in Buckinghamshire. The approaches to the river had to be made

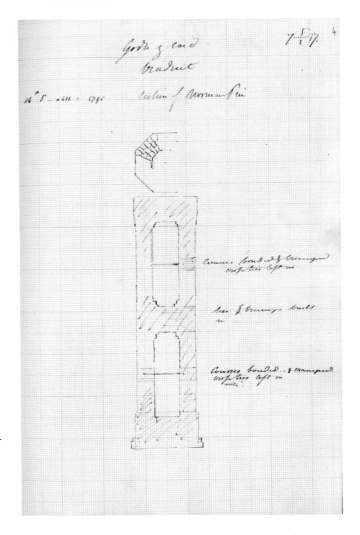

Brunel's sketch for the pier
of the Goitre Coed Viaduct –
he spells it 'Godle y Coed'.
(Ref DM162.8.1.4.TVR,
Sketchbook folio 4.
Courtesy of the Brunel
Institute, Bristol)

at some height and to raise an embankment Stephenson reckoned to use spoil from
the excavation of cuttings along the line. To transport the raw earth to the embankment's
location, it was necessary to bridge the Grand Junction Canal – a strategy to which the
canal company strongly objected, being reluctant to cooperate with the rival transport
system. At the end of 1834, Stephenson made a pre-emptive strike. By torchlight, he
supervised his labourers as they drove home the foundation piles during the night of
23/24 December and, around noon on Christmas Day, the bridge was ready for use.

Reprisals soon followed. Canal engineer John Lake assembled a gang of labourers
who demolished it, precipitating a major fracas with the railway navvies. Unimpressed,
the railway company sought recourse through the courts. Early in January 1835 they
obtained an injunction to restrain the canal men from 'putting down, taking up or
destroying' any of their works and construction of the embankment resumed.

Despite the best efforts of Stephenson and his workforce, it continued to give trouble.
Built upon the old course of the diverted Ouse, the earthwork repeatedly subsided

Detail showing the octagonal piers that Brunel planned for the Goitre Coed Viaduct, with later bracing. When Sir John Hawkshaw oversaw its widening in the early 1860s, he introduced a second set of piers, which have a standard rectangular outline.

Built in the 1830s, the Wolverton Viaduct was widened to accommodate two additional lines of track in 1878–82; the join is visible below the arches. (SP 815 422)

into the clayey ground. Eventually, the contractors endeavoured to stabilise it by digging in alum shale. It proved disastrous. The shale contained iron sulphate, which spontaneously combusted as it decomposed. Local opinion attributed the fire variously to divine judgement on the railway company, presumably for their effrontery in seeking to improve upon Creation, and a desperate attempt by the strapped-for-cash directors to foil their creditors. Flippancy aside, an unusual amount of trouble beset the Wolverton Viaduct, which was not completed until 1838, making it one of the line's last major works to be finished.

Many of the problems to trouble early viaduct builders arose from landowners' hostility to the whole railway scene. Authorised in August 1859, work on building the Brecon & Merthyr Railway began in January 1860; its engineers were Henry Conybeare and Alexander Sutherland, with David Davies and Thomas Savin working in partnership

An illustration of the Wolverton Viaduct from Thomas Roscoe's guidebook, *The London and Birmingham Railway with Home and Country Scenes on Each Side of the Line.* The peaceful scene belies the difficulties that attended the viaduct's construction. (Courtesy of the Institution of Civil Engineers)

as contractors. Three years later, 19 miles of track was opened between Brecon and Pant. At that point, a difficulty arose over making the connection through to Merthyr Tydfil; ironmaster Robert Crawshay objected to the railway's crossing the grounds of Cyfarthfa Castle, his family home. To add to the complications, the partnership of Davies and Savin dissolved around this time, and while Davies left the venture, Savin – draper, hotelier, sometime mayor of Oswestry and energetic promoter of railways and railway-related tourism throughout Wales – over-reached himself and went bankrupt.

The chagrined railway company asked Sutherland to resolve matters. A friend of Crawshay's, he re-designed the route, taking the line west of Cyfarthfa so as to leave the castle and estate unscathed. It meant building two sizeable and expensive viaducts, however, and tradition maintains that there had been an element of bribery in play. It would probably be unfair to make capital from the detail that when Crawshay died in 1879, his will, widely reported in the newspapers of the time, included a bequest to Sutherland of £100.

Standing high above the Taf Fawr, the viaduct at Cefn Coed y Cymmer is both graceful and robust. Some grievance over the employment of non-union labour led the stonemasons to strike in early 1866, so Sutherland purchased bricks at short notice with which to line the arch soffits. In August 1866, his wife ceremonially set the last stone in the structure with a fine silver trowel. Amid the celebrations that followed, the platform used for the banquet collapsed and some of the workforce, having made the most of the free beer which the company generously provided, ended up in the lock-up.

At eight arches, neighbouring Pont Sarn Viaduct, which crosses the Taf Fechan, is smaller, but still striking – particularly to anyone approaching it from under the road bridge, past the site of the long-vanished Pont Sarn station. Located in pastureland, it was for years a popular destination for chapel outings and picnics – a relatively unusual claim to viaduct fame. The nearby Hengoed Viaduct was built to take the Taff Vale Extension Railway over the River Rhymney. In a location where rival railways jostle for space, a skewed arch at its easternmost end accommodates the old Brecon & Merthyr line, which snakes beneath it.

Cefn Coed Viaduct, with its brick-lined arch soffits. (SO 030 077)

Pont Sarn Viaduct, now surrounded by woodland. When the railway was operational, the station and hotel at its western end made the viaduct a popular venue for chapel outings. (SO 045 099)

An Adulam Chapel Sunday School outing to Pont Sarn Viaduct, *c.* 1930. (Collection of Steve Brewer)

A deck-level view of the sixteen-arch Hengoed Viaduct. Built to take the Taff Vale Extension Railway over the Rhymney Valley, it dominates the village of Maesycwmmer, which it crosses. (ST 156 949)

In September 1860, Joseph Mitchell, engineer to the Perth & Inverness Junction Railway, called on the 6th Duke of Atholl to outline its route. Despite a powerful dislike of railways, the Duke treated him with the utmost courtesy. He had known Mitchell's father, who had assisted Thomas Telford with planning the Parliamentary Highland Roads and Bridges, and he welcomed the young engineer to Blair Castle as his guest.

'How odd,' he remarked, as they sat down to dine. 'Your father built the Tilt Bridge and made the new road below the castle, and now you are come to make the railway....'

The following day, the Duke and Duchess took Mitchell in their carriage to inspect the country through which the railway would pass. Still implacably opposed to it, Duke protested that its construction would mean the loss of three of the estate oak trees. At once, his wife intervened. She asserted, first, that in a 'wooded country ... some sacrifices had to made'; second, that the Atholl estate had 'no want of fine trees'; and third, that her husband 'could very easily spare a few' for 'so important a purpose' as building a railway. On his side, Mitchell, who recounts the exchange in his *Reminiscences*, promised that the railway would not encroach upon the Blair Castle carriage drive, and that where it crossed the parkland, it would be 'an ornament rather than an eyesore'.

The Tilt Viaduct gives a fair indication of his sense of the ornamental. Since it has only a single span, it may have acquired the name of 'Viaduct' either to distinguish it from the bridge on the Parliamentary Road or because – Repton-wise – Mitchell surmised that the Latinate term would heighten its prestige. It is a lattice girder bridge with stone turrets at either end, which Mitchell considered 'more ornate than was ... necessary'.

His ten-span stone viaduct which skirts the eastern side of the Pass of Killiecrankie – also on Atholl land – strays towards gothic extravagance. Its castellations probably serve some strengthening function while playing upon the Jacobite associations of the place. Both structures exemplify stone and mortar diplomacy at its most persuasive. Having said that, it is possible that Mitchell's plain box girder viaduct over the River Findhorn near Forres gives an idea of the form that his design inclinations took when he felt free to follow them.

Tilt Viaduct – the single-span viaduct that Joseph Mitchell designed to please the railway-averse 6th Duke of Atholl. (NN 873 651)

The Inverness & Perth Junction Railway Viaduct, which skirts the River Geary in the Pass of Killiecrankie. (NN 916 625)

The 1858 box girder viaduct which Joseph Mitchell designed to cross the River Findhorn near Forres. (NJ 020 586)

Chapter 6

Timber and Iron

Early in the nineteenth century, Pomeranian engineer Carl Friedrich von Wiebeking developed a system for building arches in section, using laminated timber which had been kyanized – that is, treated with bichloride of mercury – both to preserve it and give it some fire-proofing. The building technique appears to have been well-established in continental Europe, and in 1839 John and Benjamin Green adopted it for constructing the timber arches for viaducts on the Newcastle & North Shields Railway at Ouseburn and Willington Dene. Significantly, the railway company insisted that the piers of both bridges be made strong enough to allow for the timbers' eventual replacement with a more durable material. The present wrought iron structures went up in 1869, but follow the design of their wooden predecessors. Creating the latticework played to the skills of the Tyneside angle-smiths – ironworkers who forged the angular pieces used in a ship's bracing.

Apart from the Ouseburn and Willington bridges, the Wiebeking technique of building with wood never gained widespread popularity in Britain. Nevertheless, the idea of introducing economical timber viaducts held understandable appeal, particularly by to railway companies operating in hilly areas that required several crossings. Built as a short-term measure to enable the line to open, they could be replaced with permanent structures once the railway was making money. Around 1840, I. K. Brunel designed

Ouseburn Viaduct (1839), located at Newcastle-upon-Tyne, is seen with the Byker Metro Viaduct (1980) and the Byker Road Bridge (1878) in the background. (NZ 261 647)

Willington Dene Viaduct, Newcastle-upon-Tyne. The ironwork both here and at Ouseburn dates from 1869 and replicates the original timber construction. The Green brothers appear to have formed wooden arches around substantial ribs, which are visible in the Ouseburn photograph. A central arm runs from the crown of each arch to meet the stone piers on either side of it at an oblique angle. Vertical wooden struts (now replaced by wrought iron) fill the spandrel space above this central arm, while radiating struts occupy the area below it. (NZ 317 667)

a wooden bridge to take a minor road over a railway cutting near Sonning, and the experience convinced him of the material's utility. Before long, his economical timber viaducts would carry ambitious if impecunious railways over the steep-sided valleys of South West England and South Wales. In design terms they varied widely; sometimes simple timber trestles supported the deck, and sometimes – particularly in the deeper valleys – timber struts spread like a fan from the tops of tall masonry piers to support the beams beneath the track. Cheap to build, they were also cheap to maintain. An inspection team surveyed them at three-monthly intervals, removing and replacing the superannuated or defective spars.

If these bridges had many advantages for railways companies, they were not entirely popular with passengers. Not only did they look fragile, but they were apt to creak alarmingly as trains crossed them. To judge from the precarious appearance of the trestle viaduct that once carried the Oxford, Worcester & Wolverhampton Railway over the Hoo Brook valley in Kidderminster – by the 1850s, timber bridges were in use across the Midlands – the anxiety was understandable. None of Brunel's timber viaducts survive now in their original form. Some, like Moorswater, have been replaced by masonry viaducts; others, like Liskeard, have had steel or wrought iron trusses substituted in place of the old wooden superstructure.

A photograph dating from the early 1880s shows the trestle and fan design of the timber viaduct at Hoo Brook on the eastern fringe of Kidderminster. (SO 836 749) (Courtesy of Kidderminster Public Library)

The Brick viaduct being built alongside the old wooden viaduct [1880]

Another view of Kidderminster's timber Hoo Brook Viaduct, with work on building the brick viaduct which has replaced it in progress. (Courtesy of Kidderminster Public Library)

Moorswater Viaduct, Cornwall. The piers of Brunel's timber viaduct stand high and empty beside its stone successor. (SX 237 639)

Yet some wooden viaducts – though none from the Brunel era – remain in regular use. Built for the Aberystwyth & Welsh Coast Railway in the 1860s, the wooden Barmouth Bridge which spans the Mawddach Estuary owes its design to Thomas Savin who, with Henry Conybeare, oversaw its construction. It opened to horse-drawn traffic on 3 June 1867 and to locomotives the following October.

In Scotland, a four-span trestle viaduct designed by Murdoch Paterson in the 1890s carries the remote line between Inverness and Moy over a boggy stream at Aultnaslanach. In the 1990s, wet rot was discovered in the woodwork. In the course of renovating the bridge, concrete pillars designed to support a new steel deck were installed within the timber frame at a cost of over £2 million. Whether this work amounted to building a new bridge in the old shell is open to argument, but the trestlework at least preserves some sense of the structure's distinctive character.

In 1846, Robert Stephenson introduced a cast-iron, three-arch viaduct to take the Chester & Holyhead Railway across the Dee at Chester. It collapsed the following year, plunging a Ruabon-bound train into the river and killing four passengers and the fireman. Not surprisingly, the disaster cast a long shadow. Newly appointed Railway Commission Inspector-General Captain John Lintorn Arabin Simmons (1821–1903) identified its cause as the fracture of one of the bridge girders. Not only did public

Barmouth Bridge, seen from the south. The wooden viaduct celebrated its 150th anniversary in 2017. (SH 620 154).

Barmouth Bridge, seen from the north. The largely timber-built viaduct includes five (originally eight) wrought iron spans at its northern end. One of them was modified in the early twentieth century to serve as a swing bridge, to open for shipping. No longer operative, it replaced the drawbridge incorporated in the original design.

Built to cross some very marshy ground, engineer Murdoch Paterson chose timber in preference to masonry for the 1897 Aultnaslanach Viaduct's construction. (NH 760 349)

confidence in iron railway bridges falter, but Simmons himself, representing the Board of Trade, was most unwilling to authorise John Fowler's pioneering girder bridge at Torksey for railway use.

Amid the furore, distinguished engineer Sir William Fairbairn submitted a paper on 'Tubular Girder Bridges' for the Institution of Civil Engineers' consideration. When it came up for discussion, Simmons was present and the ensuing debate rapidly turned into a dispute between a Government official, reluctant to lose face, on the one hand, and the members of a rising profession, keen to resist any state interference in the way they exercised their judgement, on the other. Simmons admitted that in the load test he had conducted on the bridge, wherein he brought four locomotives onto it, he mistakenly took their total weight to be 80 tons when it was in fact 148 tons. Acknowledging his error, he nevertheless insisted on making further tests. When they demonstrated that the bridge sank only a tenth of an inch under a loading of 144 tons, Simmons conceded that it was safe.

Robert Stephenson chose to bridge the Tyne at a high level in order to avoid any need for trains to tackle lengthy gradients on either side of the crossing and his construction of a bridge with two decks – railway above road – would save both money and space in a densely populated area. Queen Victoria visited Newcastle in 1894, shortly after the High Level Bridge's opening. Learning that her schedule would not allow time for a civic reception at the Castle, the railway authorities agreed that the Royal Train should stop on Stephenson's viaduct for the mayor to make his loyal address. Despite steady rain, crowds came out to listen and to watch Victoria and Albert admire the shipping

The Torksey Viaduct was built in 1847–49 and was designed by John Fowler to take the Manchester, Sheffield & Lincolnshire Railway over the River Trent. The iron girders were inserted in 1897 to strengthen it as traffic loading increased. No longer in railway use, it remains open to pedestrians. (SK 836 791)

Above: Believed to be both the first bridge in the world to carry rail and road traffic on one structure, Newcastle High Level Bridge is also one of the earliest examples of a wrought iron tied arch or bowstring girder bridge. (NZ 251 636)

Right: The arches of the High Level Bridge support the railway and the wrought iron hangers seen here suspend the roadway.

on the Tyne. The only disappointment occurred when the double-headed Royal Train left Newcastle at a furious 20 mph instead of the 'walking pace' promised by notices in the local press.

Nowhere, perhaps, did an iron viaduct make a greater impact than the village of Crumlin in South Wales, where the Taff Vale Extension of the Newport, Abergavenny & Hereford Railway crossed the Ebbw and Kendon valleys. The cost of constructing a masonry viaduct at this location promised to be prohibitive; besides, Charles Liddell, the railway's engineer, feared that a stone bridge would never withstand the prevailing winds. Having invited tenders for the construction of a wrought iron crossing, the railway company awarded the contract for what would be Britain's tallest ever railway viaduct to Thomas William Kennard of Falkirk.

Once Kennard had settled on the number and location of the piers, and prepared their foundation, construction began. Each pier was made up of fourteen cast-iron cylindrical columns, 12 inches in outside diameter. Arranged in three rows of four, and with an additional column at each end, they were hexagonal in shape. Bands of horizontal bracing connected them. Each column rested on a base plate that was bolted into the foundation, with molten sulphur poured into the crevices to secure it. The deck was supported by wrought iron girders – four in each span arranged as two pairs. Each girder took the form of a truss – in effect an open framework – of seventeen equilateral triangles. James Warren

The Ebbw Valley section of the Crumlin Viaduct, *c.* 1906. Before it opened, the railway unsurprisingly had some difficulty in finding anyone who was willing to drive the lead locomotive of the six used for the load test. Eventually, one John Thomas Jenkins of Pontypool volunteered for the task. Disregarding his instructions to proceed slowly, he built up steam pressure and made the crossing as quickly as he could. Confronted by an appalled inspector afterwards, he observed that when eternity stared you in the face, you might as well meet it at full speed. (ST 211 985) (Author's Collection)

and Willoughby Theobald Monzani had patented the design in 1848 and Kennard adapted it to suit local conditions. While the wrought iron was light, the triangles made for strength. Prefabricated on site, the ease of connecting the separate elements enabled the workforce to assemble a girder in two days, hoisting it into position and bolting it into place on the third. When the girders were secure, the labourers set timber baulks on top of them to form a floor, upon which they laid sleepers and two tracks of rail.

Early in 1857, Lt-Col. George Wynne, Senior Government Inspector of Railways, arrived to conduct a load test. Six locomotives, each carrying pig iron in every available space, went over the viaduct's entire length, while resident engineer Mark Carr recorded the structure's movement. At one point, he scrambled over the handrail and, clinging to the ironwork at the side of the deck, conducted an almost airborne inspection of the separate parts, to see if any looked likely to give way; in fact, every fastening remained firm. Even when the live load on the bridge increased, deflection of the ironwork varied only between 7/8 of an inch and 1¼ inches, which was judged to be well within the limits of toleration. On 1 June 1857, the Crumlin Viaduct opened to traffic amid cheers, music and cannon-fire.

As the years passed, it caused increasing concern, however. Liddell's anxieties about the wind were well-founded; buffeted by the Welsh gales, the viaduct needed constant maintenance. By 1960, traffic crossing it was subject to stringent weight limits and a speed limit of 8 mph. In 1964, the railway closed, and despite its being scheduled for preservation, the viaduct's demolition followed three years later. Now, only the abutments remain.

One of the Crumlin Viaduct's surviving abutments towers above Cwm Kendon.

The same fate has overtaken Thomas Bouch's wrought and cast-iron Belah Viaduct. Built for the South Durham & Lancashire Union Railway, promoter Henry Pease laid its foundation stone in November 1857. Having opened in 1860, the viaduct had more than a century's working life, but January 1962 saw the last train to cross it and it was demolished the following year. Dating from the 1870s, Bennerley Viaduct has been more fortunate. Situated in the Erewash Valley, it owes its origins to the GNR's bid to break the Midland Railway's monopolistic grasp on routes to the Derbyshire and Nottinghamshire coalfields. Since the presence of old workings below the valley bottom ruled out any question of building in masonry, which would have always been at risk of subsidence, GNR engineer Richard Johnson designed the massive viaduct of wrought iron, with resident engineer Samuel Abbott overseeing its construction. Scheduled for demolition following the railway's closure, the contractor declined the work because it promised to be too expensive. The viaduct remains *in situ*, and is now a Grade II listed structure.

Meldon Viaduct in Devon, which also dates from the 1870s, is diminutive by comparison. Its working life suggests that it was never entirely satisfactory. When it opened, an axle load limit was imposed, restricting the bridge's usage to certain classes of locomotive. It returned to single track working in 1966 but closed to rail traffic two years later.

In the light of this melancholy chronicle, it is worth adding that the use of girders with masonry in bridge design increased as the nineteenth century advanced. A nine-span viaduct designed by Murdoch Paterson to cross a wide valley at Tomatin shows the style at its most spectacular. Reaching a height of 143 feet above the River Findhorn, it makes an immense impact and, to Paterson's credit, remains in railway use.

Although the Belah Viaduct has been demolished, the stone abutments on either side of the Belah Valley and the derelict signal box on the western side serve as a reminder of the traffic it once carried. (NY 837 104).

The Bennerley Viaduct, vast in
the Erewash Valley. (SK 472 438)

See from ground level, it becomes
clear that the Meldon Viaduct
form consists of two bridges
built adjacent to one another.
Designed by W. R. Galbraith for
the London & South Western
Railway, its first train crossed on
1 October 1874; four years later,
it was doubled to accommodate a
second track. (SX 564 923)

Murdoch Paterson's steel
lattice viaduct high above the
River Findhorn at Tomatin.
(NH 807 288)

Chapter 7

Case Study: The Viaducts of the Settle–Carlisle Railway

Dating from the 1870s, the Settle–Carlisle Railway marked a triumphant flourish of masonry viaduct construction. Excluding the smaller ones around Settle, there are seventeen sizeable bridges along the 73-mile route. One of Britain's last main lines to be built, its origins lay in the competition that existed between the Midland and the London & North Western Railways.

In the 1860s, the Midland Railway directors wished to develop their Scotland-bound traffic. Since Midland rails ran to Ingleton, where the LNWR also had a station, the company's first rather naïve plan was to co-operate with the LNWR over timetabling. As a rival, the LNWR was quick to twist matters to its advantage, however.

In the summer months, an LNWR express left London daily and divided at Preston. One part of the train ran swiftly on to Glasgow and Edinburgh by way of Carlisle, but rather than pick up Midland passengers at Ingleton, the arrangement was that they waited to join the slow train to Tebay, along with the LNWR coal wagons. The rival companies' inability to agree terms on which to share an Ingleton station was another source of annoyance. Having reached the Midland Railway's Ingleton station, to catch a Scotland-bound connection, Midland passengers had to make their way across a steep valley to the LNWR's Ingleton station, a mile to the north of the town.

Eventually, the Midland Railway lost patience. With support from the North British and Yorkshire & Lancashire railways, the company obtained an Act of Parliament authorising them to build from Settle in Yorkshire through the bleak fells to connect with the Scots railway companies at Carlisle. Alarmed, the LNWR promised to make better arrangements for its Midland passengers – a pledge which almost persuaded the Midland men to withdraw their plans – but seeing how they stood to benefit from the new line, the Midland's North British and Yorkshire & Lancashire allies resisted any notion of a corporate change of mind. Parliament, meanwhile, having observed the scheme's popularity, refused the railway's application to abandon it. In other words, the die was cast.

Orphaned in infancy, John Sydney Crossley (1812–79) who masterminded the Settle–Carlisle Railway's construction was brought up by a guardian – a surveyor named Christopher Staveley, who worked for the Leicester Navigation Company.

Completed in 1860, Ingleton Viaduct was a focal point of the rivalry between the LNWR and Midland Railway which led to the Settle–Carlisle Railway's construction. Mutual animosity between the companies led each to establish its own station at Ingleton – the Midland to the south of the viaduct, the LNWR to the north. Midland passengers were not carried over its arches, but had to walk to the LNWR station instead, with orders not to cross the bridge, but to follow the road through the valley. (SD 693 731)

Staveley articled his ward to his son Edward, a canal engineer from whom Crossley learned the rudiments of his profession. In 1833, Edward Staveley, newly married and to all appearance respectably settled in his work, embezzled £1,400 from Leicester Navigation Company funds and skipped the country; his brother, Christopher Staveley Junior, who was implicated in the theft, committed suicide, and Crossley joined the Leicester & Swannington Railway to assist engineer William Provis with making the Parliamentary surveys.

In 1837, he married Agnes Combe and, announcing the wedding, the *Leicester Chronicle* described him – surprisingly – as a 'Bookseller'. Since there was a flourishing firm of Leicester booksellers at this time named Combe & Crossley – the 'Combe' partner was Agnes's father – the slip was understandable; indeed, John Sydney's birth family may have been the Crossley element in the concern. But railway engineering was evidently his chosen calling and by 1853 Crossley was working for Charles Liddell on the Leicester & Hitchin line. Five years later, the Midland Railway appointed him as their engineer in chief.

The Ribblehead Viaduct from the north. Faced with limestone from the nearby Little Dale quarries, the arches are built of brick with rubble-filled cores. The voussoirs, spandrels and parapets are built of limestone, steam engines being used to raise the large blocks into position. True to his Leicestershire roots, Crossley brought in the hydraulic lime mortar in which to set the stonework from his home town of Barrow upon Soar. (SD 759 794)

The date '1875' on Ribblehead Viaduct's central pier marks its opening, although the *Lancashire Gazette* reported that a party of railway shareholders made an unofficial crossing on the locomotive *Diamond* the previous year.

Together with Midland manager James Allport, he reconnoitred for the proposed line from Settle to Carlisle in 1863. Despite the rough and remote terrain, both men thought that building the railway would be achievable. Before applying to Parliament, they engaged a young Tasmanian named Charles Sharland (1844–71) to take levels and make a detailed survey of the proposed line.

Construction started in 1869. For contracting purposes, the company divided the route into four sections. The original contractors were John Ashwell (Contract No. 1, from Settle station to the Dent marble works between Dent and Hawes); Messrs Benton and Woodiwiss (Contract No. 2, some 17 miles of demanding terrain between Dent Head and Smardale); Mr Firbank (Contract No. 3 from Smardale to Newbiggin); and Messrs Eckersley and Bayliss (Contract No 4, Newbiggin to Petteril Bridge in the Parish of St Cuthbert, Carlisle). Five short viaducts north of Settle fell into Contract No. 1, together with the twenty-four-arch Ribblehead Viaduct, the Blea Moor tunnel and a viaduct of ten arches at Dent Head. Contract No. 2 covered viaducts at

Arten Gill, Dandry Mire, Ais Gill, Lunds and Smardale. Contract No. 3 included the viaducts at Crosby Garrett, Griseburn, Ormside, Long Marton and Crowdundle. To Contract No. 4 went the viaducts at Little Salkeld, Eden Lacey, Armathwaite, Dry Beck and Cotehele.

When itinerant labourers arrived with their families to take up employment, by way of accommodation the company provided them with wooden huts roofed with tarred felt. Around the site of the Ribblehead Viaduct, settlements grew up with names such as Batty Green, Inkermann, Sebastopol, Jericho, Salt Lake City and Belgravia. When Midland Railway chronicler F. S. Williams visited in the 1870s, he noticed a post office, public library, mission, 'inevitable public-houses' and, unsurprisingly, a hospital. The presence of visiting tradesmen, be they greengrocers, potters or dealers offering horses for hire, suggests that the inhabitants were not short of ready cash. Even so, recruiting labour was not easy. The demanding, dangerous nature of the work, the remoteness of the Cumbrian fells and their almost constant wet and cold tested endurance to the limit. The summer of 1872 saw so much rain, even by Cumbrian standards, that the contractors reduced the length of the working week from six days to three and increased wages in a desperate bid to retain the workforce.

The Settle–Carlisle Railway was the last main line in England to be built by hand. The usage of local stone for building the viaducts, be it red sandstone as at Smardale

F. S. Williams' *The Midland Railway: Its Rise and Progress* (1877) illustrates some of the Settle–Carlisle Railway viaducts at different stages of construction. This picture shows the Ribblehead Viaduct as it might have appeared in the early 1870s. Work has just begun on raising the piers on the right-hand side; a construction gantry surrounds those in the middle, which have reached a fair height. Semi-circular wooden 'centres' rest between the piers shown at the left-hand side of the picture – the north end of the viaduct. These were used to serve as a framework around which to build the arches. One of the temporary settlements that grew up around the viaduct to house labourers and their families is visible in the background. (Author's Collection)

Dent Viaduct, as seen from the road. (SD 777 844)

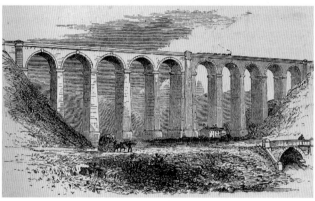

Williams' illustration of Dent Viaduct. While the carter lashes the horse struggling to pull an overloaded wagon, high above their heads a diminutive locomotive effortlessly hauls a train across the ten arches. (Author's Collection)

and Crosby Garrett, or the dark grey-black limestone known as Dent Marble at Dent Head and Arten Gill, may account for their appearance of permanence within the surrounding landscape. To their design Crossley introduced 'king piers' – piers of extra width and strength – which divide the structure into sections on the principle that if a single arch should fail, the king piers would stem any progressive structural collapse, otherwise known as the 'domino effect'. At Ribblehead, the longest viaduct on the line, this pattern is particularly striking, the king piers grouping the twenty-four segmental arches into four sets of six.

Williams, who writes about the Settle–Carlisle Railway with enthusiasm and fondness, found its viaducts a delight. The spectacle of the ten-arch Dent Head's crossing what he calls a 'magnificent' valley complete with 'a little mountain torrent', a tributary of the Dee, thrilled him, as did the ingenuity of the contractors at Arten Gill, where the steep banks of the stream as it flowed down the hillside presented them with a major challenge when they came to excavate the viaduct's foundations. At Dandry Mire the intention had been to build an embankment, but raising an earthwork upon the peat bog proved impossible and so, for the deepest part of the marsh, Crossley and the contractors opted to build the Moorcock Viaduct. Along the line to the north stand

Arten Gill Viaduct spans a high, steep-sided ravine. It is built from a form of limestone with a high fossil content that was quarried nearby, which acquired the name of 'Dent Marble' because polishing made the dark stone with its pale fossil patterns look like marble when used in tiling and for fireplaces. (SD 776 859)

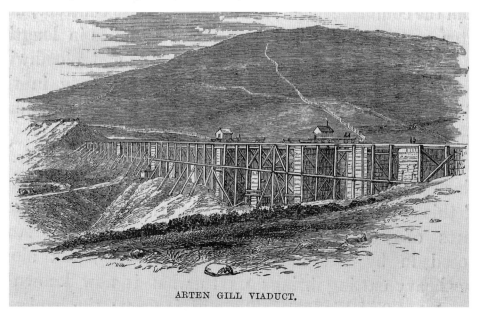

ARTEN GILL VIADUCT.

In Williams' Arten Gill Viaduct illustration, a timber gantry – in effect, scaffolding – stands on either side of the part-built structure to accommodate the labourers building the piers and abutments. (Author's Collection)

Dandry Mire Viaduct.
(SD 793 923)

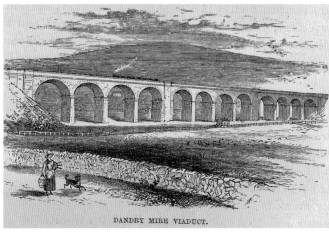

Williams' illustration of the
Dandry Mire or Moorcock
Viaduct. The name
'Moorcock' was borrowed
from the nearby Moorcock
Inn. (Author's Collection)

Lunds Viaduct. (SD 792 933)

the Lunds and Ais Gill viaducts, which, at five and four arches respectively, are two of its more modest structures. At the location of Smardale Viaduct, whose twelve arches curve across both the Scandal Beck and South Durham & Lancashire Union Railway, finding a strong foundation was unexpectedly problematic and it took digging through 45 feet of clay to reach honest red shale. A six-arch viaduct of pinkish limestone crosses the village of Crosby Garrett, while the seven-arch Griseburn Viaduct stands 3 miles to the north. The Ormside Viaduct, which crosses the River Eden, marked a change of landscape; to Williams, the Eden Valley was 'full of loveliness' – a welcome change from the high moors.

Having crossed the Long Marton Viaduct, the railway approached Newbiggin. At the time of its promotion, one William Crackanthorpe, a relative of the poet Wordsworth, lived at Newbiggin Hall, near the site of the Crowdundle Viaduct. Williams relates that surveyor Charles Sharland called and, finding Mr Crackanthorpe aghast at the prospect of the line going through his woodland, arranged for Allport and Crossley to visit and discuss matters further. For a time, landowner, manager and engineer talked amicably over the plans and, pleased to find Crackanthorpe so civil, the Midland gentlemen acceded to his request that the railway spare his finest oak tree.

'Do you know what I want it for?' Crackanthorpe asked.

'No, sir,' replied his guests, 'but whatever you want it for, it shall be saved.'

'Well,' returned Crackanthorpe, 'it's to hang you and all the engineers of the Midland Railway upon it, for daring to come here at all.'

Ais Gill Viaduct. (SD 773976)

SMARDALE VIADUCT IN COURSE OF CONSTRUCTION.

Above: Smardale is the highest viaduct on the line. Its foundations were sunk some 45 feet (14 metres) below ground surface. It is built from high quality limestone from a quarry near the site; easily worked, it readily lent itself to construction of the viaduct's piers, with the darker millstone grit being used in the parapets and voussoirs. (NY 733 081)

Left: Smardale. Williams' illustration shows the timber staging surrounding the work in progress. The figures, drawn in engaging detail, give an idea of the immense size of the stone blocks. (Author's Collection)

Crosby Garrett Viaduct. (NY 727 093)

Ormside Viaduct crosses the River Eden about 42 miles north of Settle. (NY 697178)

Ormside Viaduct from a sketch by F. S. Williams, who thought it had a 'noble appearance'. (Author's Collection)

A storm closes in on Long Marton Viaduct, with snow visible on the surrounding hills. (NY 669 244)

Crowdundle Viaduct. (NY 622 285)

Williams' illustration of Crowdundle shows not only the staging, with a crane at work, but also the arch centring in place. Once the mortar had dried and hardened and the arch was ready for keying, the centres would be removed, the spandrels made up to the required height and the parapet set in place. (Author's Collection)

Little Salkeld Viaduct. (NY 566 352)

Little Salkeld Viaduct crosses the Briggle Beck near Dodds Mill, to which the railway brought a great increase in trade. At Eden Lacey, problems with finding a foundation beset the contractors building Long Meg Viaduct, which borrows its name from a nearby stone circle, which is named 'Long Meg and her Daughters'. Throughout the viaduct's construction, the weather was appalling, and the rain-swollen Eden flooded the piles and removed the temporary workings. Despite its peaceful appearance, the pastureland around Armathwaite Viaduct and its neighbour at Dry Beck was prone to landslips, which bedevilled both viaducts' construction. A final four-arch viaduct stands to the south of Cote Hill station, some 7 miles south of Carlisle.

Crossley resigned in 1875, but not before he had watched his wife set the final ceremonious stone in the fabric of the Smardale Viaduct, the highest on the line. She was one of the few people to recognise the parlous state of his health. In 1852, long before the origins of the Settle–Carlisle venture, he had suffered a major stroke in Charles Liddell's office. Liddell's decision a year later to appoint him resident engineer to the Leicester & Hitchin Railway says much, both for Crossley's zeal and Liddell's confidence in his abilities.

In the spring of 1876, shortly before the line's official opening, Crossley joined the Midland directors to travel over its entire length on a special train, and at the end of the journey he remarked *Finis coronat opus* [the end crowns the work]. The Latin phrase made a prescient utterance, for it enshrines the Settle–Carlisle Railway as his memorial. He died three years after its completion.

Armathwaite Viaduct. (NY 499 452)

Drybeck Viaduct. (NY 508 478)

Chapter 8

Pushing the Boundaries

To nineteenth-century railway companies, the great sea inlets in the Scottish coast represented a significant challenge. Bridging them would take skill, courage and investment, but the promise of a route that avoided either the inconvenience of a detour or the discomfort of a ferry-passage counted for much. Robert Stephenson had bridged the mouth of the Tweed; the next great geographical obstacles to overcome were the firths of Solway, Tay and Forth.

The Solway Junction Railway was conceived as a route by which to bring haematite ore from Cumberland to the ironworks of Lanarkshire and Ayrshire. Plans for building a viaduct from Bowness-on-Solway to Annan developed in the 1860s; it held the promise both of linking with existing railways on either side of the Firth and avoiding any need to go through Carlisle with its congestion and delays. In his evidence to Parliament, James William Brunlees (1816–92) – the Solway Junction's engineer – gave a clear assurance that the viaduct's construction would not interfere with shipping on the Firth, and that building the solid approach embankments would probably have the effect of deepening and widening the navigation channel. The fact that the new company was more interested in freight carriage than passenger traffic may have encouraged Parliament to view the plans more in the light of far-sighted commercial enterprise than a hazard in the making. Despite opposition from the established Glasgow & South Western Railway, which feared the loss of its traffic to the upstart competitor, the incorporation of the Solway Junction Railway took place on 30 June 1864.

In securing the services of Brunlees the railway was fortunate, since he specialised in estuarial projects. Early in his career, he had made a success of setting out an embankment to take the Londonderry & Coleraine Railway across the shifting sands and mudflats of Rosse's Bay on the southern side of the Foyle estuary. Later, he designed piers for Llandudno and Southport, docks for Avonmouth and Lynn and long viaducts to cross the rivers Leven and Kent on the margins of Morecambe Bay. In the course of this work, he pioneered the use of jetted piling – that is, the technique of using water under pressure to drive piles into sandy ground, where it was impractical to rely on a steam hammer.

Brunlees' initial intention had been to have eighty spans, each of 30 feet in length, to build the embankment out as far as the low water mark on either side of the Firth, and to incorporate an opening span of 36 feet within the structure to accommodate

The embankment approaching
the Solway Viaduct near
Bowness-on-Solway.

fishing vessels and small craft. At some point intentions changed, and the opening span vanished from the plans. In its final, functioning form, the bridge included 193 spans, each of which were 30 feet in length. Its total cost was £100,000, which, besides labour, encompassed 2,892 tons of cast iron in the piles and columns, and 1,807 tons of wrought iron in the bracing and superstructure. While Brunlees designed it to a width that could accommodate a double track, only a single line was ever laid. Since the Solway site did not lend itself to jetted piling, instead a steam hammer was used at low tide to drive in the iron piles which served as foundation for the columns. No scaffolding was used in its building, but the company purchased a Clyde-built steamer, *Arabian*, to tow five barges out into the Firth to serve as impromptu work platforms.

Compared with the difficulty of building the railway over miry Bowness Moss, construction of the viaduct went ahead without undue trouble. That is not to say that there were no mishaps. Barges foundered amid high winds and had to be recovered from the bed of the Solway; in November 1866 the riveting platform collapsed, hurling a labourer to his death and concussing the boy who had been working with him. Despite these disasters, the line opened to goods trains in September 1869 and to passenger traffic a year later.

The viaduct needed regular maintenance and frequent repairs. In 1875, water froze inside some of the columns and fractured them; then, at the end of the harsh winter of 1880/81, broken ice damaged the viaduct's piers so badly that it closed for three years to allow for re-building and modification. By the mid-1890s the iron traffic for which the railway had been built was in decline, although trains continued to take passengers

At 1,950 yards long, at the time of its completion the Solway Viaduct was the longest bridge in Europe. The piers were each made up of five hollow cast-iron columns – each 12 inches in diameter with the two on the outside being set at a slight rake so as to buttress the four in the centre which took the main load. (NY 212 627)

and livestock across the Solway. The viaduct survived into the twentieth century, closing to passenger traffic during the First World War and to goods trains in 1921. Even then, it remained in unofficial pedestrian use by the people of Annan, which observed a dry Scots Sabbath, who walked across it on Sundays to visit the pubs of the Godless southern shore. Concern – was it for their safety or their morals? – led the authorities to call for the viaduct's demolition and it was dismantled in 1933.

If the Solway Junction Railway and its viaduct were chiefly of local interest, the vision of a train plunging from the high girders of Sir Thomas Bouch's Tay Bridge into the Firth beneath shocked the nation. The sequence of events from the bridge's triumphal opening in 1878 and Bouch's being honoured with a knighthood to its failure a year later, and the Court of Inquiry's conclusion that it was 'badly designed, badly built and badly maintained', makes a tragic tale. Not only did fifty-nine passengers lose their lives, but for Bouch the disgrace was catastrophic and it marked the end of his career.

While the precise cause of the disaster remains open to speculation, it is a matter of record both that Bouch designed the bridge without making any allowance for wind-loading upon its fabric, and that quality control, insofar as it existed at the

Thomas Bouch's Tay Bridge, opened 1 June 1878, failed in a storm on 28 December 1879. (Author's Collection)

Wormit Foundry, which produced the ironwork, was extremely lax. Yet, for all its shortcomings, Bouch's eighty-six-span lattice girder viaduct demonstrated the value of a Tay crossing. Replacing it was essential and in the 1880s the North British Railway gave the contract to Court of Inquiry member William Henry Barlow (1812–1902) and his son, Crawford.

The Barlows designed another lattice girder viaduct, but it was conspicuously more robust than its predecessor. Bouch's bridge had brick piers at its extreme southern end, but when it emerged that the bed of the Tay was gravelly rather than solid rock, he redesigned the structure to lighten the load on the foundations. For the remainder of the bridge's length, he introduced piers made from cast-iron cylindrical columns set upon masonry bases. John Fowler, engineer of the Forth Bridge, always reckoned that they had been too narrow. Had the bases been wider, he surmised, and adopted something like a Henry VIII straddle (he made the remark after visiting an exhibition of Holbein's paintings), the bridge would have been more secure.

Whether or not the Barlows knew of his views, their piers were certainly sturdier than Bouch's. Built as twins, each had a pair of tubular iron caissons as its foundation, which were sunk into the bed of the Tay and then filled with concrete. Above low water level, the ironwork was faced with bricks, and a concrete and brick beam offered additional bracing above the high water mark. A wrought iron arch connects each pair of caissons, rising to support the deck. Each cylindrical caisson underwent a load test, the load being one third more than the maximum weight permitted under working conditions.

The Barlows' bridge is somewhat longer than its predecessor, being 3,570 yards in length against Bouch's 3,456-yard bridge. The line from the south approaches it on brick arches. A central 'high girder section' accommodates shipping on the Tay. The section running north from that point into Dundee consisted of one span of 162 feet; eleven of 129 feet; twenty-four of 71 feet and one of 56 feet. Eight curving skew spans – two in wrought iron; four of cast-iron girders on columns; a 108-ft girder section on brick piers; and a brick arch joining the old line into Dundee Tay station – complete the bridge. (NO 394 269)

The present-day Tay bridge as seen from the south-east, with the piers of the old bridge visible beside it.

Acutely aware of the force of the gales in the Firth, the Barlows subjected it to comprehensive trials to ensure that it should withstand pressure of up to 56 lb per square foot. It was, apparently, the first time that a British railway bridge had been tested to assess its behaviour in strong winds.

It opened to traffic on 20 June 1887. Although the ceremonies were muted, the *Dundee Courier* made much of the number and stringency of the tests by which the Board of Trade assessed the new bridge's safety.

Besides his ill-fated Tay Bridge, Bouch had also designed a rail suspension bridge to cross the Firth of Forth. Building began in September 1878 with the laying of a foundation stone for one of the central piers on Inchgarvie. Following the Tay Bridge disaster, public confidence in Bouch ebbed, and in August 1880 the work had ceased. With the opening of the Barlows' Tay Bridge, interest in a Forth crossing revived and, in 1881, John Fowler, engineer of London's Metropolitan Railway, and his assistant Benjamin Baker submitted plans for a large-scale cantilever bridge to the Forth Bridge Company. In the same year, Parliament authorised its construction.

The cost of completing it was estimated at £300,000, to which the four railway companies that made up the Forth Bridge Railway – the North British; the North Eastern; the Great Northern; and the Midland railways, which supplied a third of the total amount – all contributed. With William Arrol & Co. of Glasgow appointed as contractor, work began on building Britain's most distinctive and recognisable bridge in June 1883. Constructed from steel tubes and latticework, it would have three towers rising some 361 feet above the usual level of high water in the firth; lattice girder sections to connect them, each spanning a distance of 1,710 feet between the towers, and lattice girder viaducts formed the approaches at each end. Underpinning the towers are granite foundations, set within wrought iron caissons below the bed of the Forth.

The bridge was seven years in the building and at full strength, the workforce amounted to 4,600 labourers, at least fifty-six of whom lost their lives during construction. Even so, the company appears to have given considerable thought to their wellbeing. Safety boats patrolled the water around the site and the men were issued with what amounted to workwear: boots and waterproofs for the party engaged in building the foundation; thick woollen jackets and stout shoes for those working on the superstructure.

By January 1890 it was finished, and shortly before the Board of Trade arrived to inspect it, some of the directors of the railway companies that had financed it arranged a private tour. They set off from Waverley station in a special train consisting of a saloon carriage and a brake van, hauled by North British Railway locomotive No. 601, and paused at Queensferry, where Fowler and Baker joined them. Some of the party rode on the footplate and, just as they approached the bridge, the driver, Robert Ramsay, shut off the steam, stood aside and urged Candida, stylish wife of William Hay, Marquess of Tweeddale and Chairman of the North British Railway Company, to take his place. According to the *Stonehaven Journal*, she opened the regulator and drove the party over a bridge at a stately 10 mph.

The bridge had its official opening on 4 March 1890. As though to bear out its wind resistance – Fowler and Baker had allowed for a pressure of 56 lbs per square foot – the ceremony took place in the teeth of a howling gale. Fittingly for this emblem of a new engineering era, the ageing Queen Victoria took no part in the proceedings, but left the ceremonial task of knocking home the final rivet to her son, the Prince of Wales, later King Edward VII.

The Isle of Inchgarvie, where Bouch planned to locate the central pier of his projected Forth Suspension Bridge, seen beyond the spans of the present Forth Bridge.

The Forth Bridge – perhaps the best-known bridge in the world. (NT 135 792)

Chapter 9

New Visions for a New Century

Twentieth-century bridges witnessed two major developments: the evolution of concrete as a building material and a new focus on roads. Although concrete had been in use through much of the nineteenth century, often in foundations – particularly underwater – or in pavements, its application to bridge construction took time to develop. Its great early champion was miner-turned-railway contractor Robert McAlpine (1847–1934), nicknamed Concrete Bob. His recognition of its versatility stemmed from the experience of making concrete doorsteps and sills in the course of his work as a house builder and contractor on Clydeside in the 1870s. Since he found bricks expensive to purchase, he tried making his own and soon experimented with using concrete blocks as a substitute. Before long, in a departure from the usual building practice, which was to treat concrete solely as an auxiliary material, he was putting up houses made entirely of concrete, proving its worth as a construction material in its own right.

By the 1890s, McAlpine had taken his sons into business. When a delay in securing legislation for the West Highland Railway's extension between Fort William and Mallaig meant that regular contractors Lucas & Aird were unavailable, they took on the project. It was one of their larger ventures and, of the many bridges that the route required, the Glenfinnan Viaduct is the best known. With twenty-one arches, each 50 feet in width, it crosses the River Finnan near Loch Shiel at a height of 100 feet. It was not the first large concrete structure to be built in Britain – that was Andrew Peterson's Sway Tower in Hampshire – but it represented important pioneer work nonetheless.

The twelve-arch viaduct at Calstock in Cornwall, which was built to take the Bere Alston & Calstock Light Railway across the Tamar, is constructed not from mass concrete, but concrete blocks. Completed by contractors Galbraith & Church in 1908, it was designed by engineer John Charles Lang. Apart from the building material, its great concession to modernity was the incorporation of a lift for raising and lowering waggons between the bridge deck and Calstock Quay. It consisted of a steel cage, large enough to accommodate a loaded four-wheeled wagon weighing up to 20 tons, and relied on a steam winding engine to raise it. Its lifespan was relatively short, being dismantled in 1934, but the elegant viaduct with its high arches and slender piers remains in use.

Since the local stone around Glenfinnan was hard schist, which promised to be difficult to work with, the merits of appointing contractors with proven skill in the use of concrete might seem obvious. McAlpine talked himself into the work of building it by emphasising that concrete would neither rust nor require regular re-painting. (NM 909 813)

Calstock, with its concrete blocks conveniently pre-cast to dimensions of 5 feet x 3 feet x 2 feet, attempts with its imposts and voussoirs to imitate a stone viaduct, and it succeeds rather well. (SX 435 685)

The position of the wagon lift at Calstock.

Owen Williams' 1920s bridge over the River Findhorn at Tomatin. Two pairs of concrete beams join at the central pier. The cast concrete road deck forms the bottom of a box, while the parapet walls create an arcade on either side of it. (NH 804 277)

Despite use of the new material, both Calstock and Glenfinnan give the impression of looking to the past. Only as the twentieth century advanced did engineer-turned-architect Owen Williams (1890–1969) take concrete in new design directions. In the First World War, Williams had developed versatile pre-cast concrete elements for incorporation within factory buildings. He also took the lead in some Government-sponsored research into the development of concrete ships and was appointed consulting engineer for the British Empire Exhibition of 1924 – work for which he received a knighthood. Recognising concrete's potential for creating a powerful aesthetic impact, he brought all his experience to bear on designing memorable bridges on the A9 route between Perth and Inverness in the mid-1920s.

Among them is a small viaduct in Tomatin; one of the two arches spans the River Findhorn while the other serves as a flood arch. Between them, a substantial central pier of angular form rises from the bank. The contracting company Sir Robert McAlpine & Sons built it for the sum of £36,120, making it the most expensive of Williams' bridges. It owes its outline to the form of a Vierendeel truss (that is, a truss with rectangular openings instead of the typical triangles), only it is made not of metal but reinforced concrete, and the openings are almost octagonal. From a distance, it looks rather forbidding, but viewed at close quarters the arcading gives a sense of space and light.

The octagonal openings in the concrete arcading of Williams' River Findhorn crossing.

One engineer's tribute to another: in an inscription on the fabric of the Findhorn Bridge, Williams commemorates Thomas Telford, who built an earlier bridge on the site.

Right: The small concrete viaduct over the Spey at Advie, Morayshire. (NJ 120 353)

Below: A plaque on the Advie Bridge states that it was opened in 1922. It attributes the viaduct's design and construction to Morayshire's county surveyor Alexander Hogg and the Yorkshire Hennebique Company, manufacturers of reinforced concrete. Francois Hennebique (1842–1921), whose name they adopted, was a pioneer of its development and use.

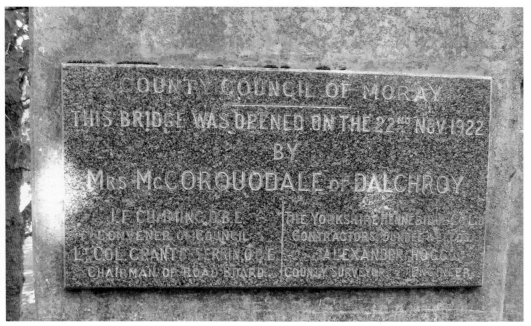

Not far away, a triple-span viaduct built from reinforced concrete crosses the Spey near the remote village of Advie. Completed in 1922, it is not perhaps as accomplished-looking as Williams' Findhorn Bridge, but shares some of the same features. Like Williams' bridge, it takes the form of a reinforced concrete truss, although its openings are true rather than approximate octagons. Its two piers take the form of paired cylindrical caissons sunk within the river bed.

During the 1930s, the LMS conducted research at their Derby laboratories into the use of pre-stressed concrete – that is, concrete cast around tensioned steel 'tendons' – for rapid building. The material proved its worth during the Second World War, when many pre-stressed concrete beams were made and stockpiled for emergency use. Where and how often they were installed is apparently unknown, but in 1946 the material came in for non-emergency, designed usage in building the Adam Viaduct on the LMS line through Wigan. A modest viaduct of four spans, it rests on the foundations of an earlier bridge and takes the railway over the River Douglas, its unassuming appearance belying its historical significance as the earliest pre-stressed railway bridge in England.

Even by the time of the Adam Viaduct's construction, British bridge building was shifting from the railways to the expanding road network, where new viaducts began to take shape. Plans to make a road crossing for the River Neath and Briton Ferry Dock, for instance, had been mooted since the 1930s, if not earlier. It would, after all, remove the need for traffic between Cardiff and Swansea either to make a long detour or take

The Adam Viaduct, Wigan, which replaced a Victorian stone viaduct in 1944. By the mid-1940s, pre-stressed and pre-cast concrete had proved its worth by offering a means of making cheap, straightforward repairs to war-damaged road bridges. The Adam Viaduct claims to be the first railway bridge in England which incorporated pre-stressed, pre-cast concrete beams for non-emergency use. (SD 572 051)

the ferry. Nothing happened at the site during the Depression and the War, but in 1949 work began on building a pair of viaducts.

The location presented consulting engineers Rendel, Palmer & Tritton with many challenges. The coast around the outfall of the River Neath was prone to erosion and stood in the teeth of south-westerly gales. Although shipping in the area had declined since the height of the nineteenth-century coal trade, enough maritime trade remained to preclude any question of bridging the river and docks at a low level, even with the inclusion of a swing or lifting element. It was agreed to allow for a clearance of about 93 feet above the River Neath at mean high water level.

At the time of construction it was Britain's largest post-war bridge project and completing the two steel viaducts which make up the crossing took six years. The western bridge has seventeen spans to its eastern sibling's eleven. A short stretch of dual carriageway connects them, crossing the small mound known as Warren Hill. When John Boyd-Carpenter MP, Minister of Transport and Civil Aviation, opened the contiguous viaducts in November 1955, he represented their building as the portent of a bright future, and enthusiastically promised that it would not be long before work began to bridge the Severn Estuary. But the British Road Federation struck a cooler note. Building the Neath Viaducts, their spokesman intimated, had taken four and a half years longer than forecast, and the roads between the Briton Ferry crossing and Swansea remained less than ideal. 'The history of this scheme must never be repeated,' he concluded.

At Neath, the western bridge – at seventeen spans and some 640 yards long – is the longer of the two viaducts. It crosses the River Neath navigation and canal. (SS 733 942)

The eastern bridge is 324 yards long and has eleven spans. It crosses both the South Wales Main Line Railway and the dock area of Briton Ferry. (SS 738 940)

Even before the Neath Viaducts opened, plans were in hand for a bridge to take the M2 over the River Medway near Rochester. Having selected the bridge's approximate location in 1954, the Ministry of Transport and Civil Aviation commissioned consulting engineers Freeman, Fox & Partners to report on the crossing and the style of bridge best suited to it. In light of their recommendations, the Ministry invited tenders for a pre-stressed concrete bridge, and, in case there should be any significant difference in coast, for steel designs of similar appearance.

Throughout the design process, great emphasis was given to the aesthetics of the scheme. All potential bridge designs were submitted to the Royal Fine Art Commission (now the Commission for Architecture and the Built Environment) for approval. Eventually, the tender from J. L. Kier & Co. and Christiani & Nielsen for a concrete bridge was chosen, its estimated £2.5 million cost being cheaper than a bridge in welded and bolted steel. Almost a mile long, the Medway Viaduct crosses the river on three spans, the central being the longest so as to allow clearance for shipping. The eastern approach viaduct has seven spans, while the western approach has eleven. The viaduct proper was built to take two lanes bound for London, two for Faversham, a hard shoulder on either side and cycle tracks cum footpaths. The Medway Viaduct opened in 1963 and the only serious misadventure to have occurred in its construction seems to have been the theft in June 1961 of wage packets containing the rather modest total sum of £800. It is uncertain whether the monies were ever recovered.

The original Medway Bridge, which opened in 1963, is at the front of the picture. The concrete beams that made up the central span of the original bridge have been replaced with steel girders. Next to it stands the 2003 bridge, which transports present-day London-bound traffic across the river. The HS1 railway bridge is just visible behind it. (TQ 723 668)

A steel composite girder viaduct, the Thelwall Viaduct opened the same year. Built to carry the M6 across the Manchester Ship Canal and the River Mersey, for years it took all six lanes of motorway – three in either direction – over the waterways, but offered no hard shoulder. Not surprisingly, it required frequent repairs and the late Brian Redhead – broadcaster and convener of the self-designating 'Friends of the M6' – made it infamous by drawing attention to the frequency with which it featured (never in any favourable aspect) in the BBC's traffic bulletins of the 1970s and '80s.

Like Medway, it would in time be doubled. A second viaduct opened in 1995 to take southbound traffic on the M6, while the motorway's northbound carriageway uses the 1963 crossing. When a roller bearing on the old bridge failed in 2002, inspection revealed that all the bearings on the bridge required immediate replacement. It closed all but one northbound lane – a parlous situation which, given the lack of any convenient diversion route, caused immense congestion and long delays. Boatmen waiting to cross the narrow aqueducts or leg through the equally narrow tunnels of the eighteenth-century canal network would fight to get to the head of queue; twenty-first-century commuters wrote aggrieved letters to their Members of Parliament. It may not have been entirely coincidental that remedial work on the viaduct was completed three months ahead of schedule.

If the episode epitomises the frustrations of motorway travel, it remains true to say that the legacy of two centuries of British bridge-building is extraordinarily rich. Structures of ineffable character, it is hardly an exaggeration to say that each of the many aqueducts and viaducts to be built between the 1760s and 1960s – be it large or small – has its own spirit and credentials. This individuality gives rise to great affection; travellers enjoy crossing them, walkers relish the sight of their spans, engineers analyse their distinctive elements and historians tell their stories. Exploring bridges is a source of endless pleasure.

With thirty-six spans, and at 4,414 feet long and rising to a height of 93 feet above the ship canal, the Thelwall Viaduct is not easy to photograph. These two spans cross the River Mersey. (SJ 664 882)

The pleasures of bridge-hunting, as shown with this view of the forty-two-arch Yarm Viaduct on a fine evening.

Further Reading

Online Sources

Among the best online sources of information about specific aqueducts and viaducts, www.engineering-timelines.com provides detailed information about historically significant structures; http://happypontist.blogspot.co.uk offers learned, if idiosyncratic, discussion of bridges and bridge-building in Britain and across the world; http://ukaqueducts.blogspot.com/ includes a collection of pictures of UK aqueducts with brief historical commentary; http://www.forgottenrelics.co.uk/ gives well-informed, chatty accounts of important railway viaducts (and tunnels), which, as its name suggests, have been sidelined; http://www.transporttrust.com lists and illustrates heritage sites to which it has awarded 'Red Wheel' plaques.

Details concerning motorway viaducts can be found on www.roads.org.uk and https://www.sabre-roads.org.uk.

Historic England – www.historicengland.org.uk – contains information about listed structures in England; Coflein – http://www.coflein.gov.uk/ – provides an online catalogue of the archaeology, buildings and industrial and maritime heritage of Wales; Canmore – https://www.canmore.org.uk / – offers the same service for Scotland.

Access to digitised archive publications is available via Grace's Guide – https://www.gracesguide.co.uk/View_by_Archives.

The British Newspaper Archive https://www.britishnewspaperarchive.co.uk requires a subscription and provides access to historical newspapers.

Books

Specific Canals, Railways and Bridges

Anon., *The Advantage of Railways with Locomotive Engines, Especially the London and Greenwich Railway or Viaduct* (London: 1833).

Anon., *History of Inland Navigations, Particularly those of the Duke of Bridgewater in Lancashire and Cheshire* (London: Printed for T. Lowndes, 1769 edition).

Atkinson, Glen, *Building Barton's Bridges, or, Barton's Bridges Falling Down* (Manchester, Neil Richardson, 2002).

Booth, Henry, *An Account of the Liverpool & Manchester Railway* (Liverpool: Wales and Baines, 1830).

Compton, Hugh, *The Oxford Canal* (Newton Abbot: David and Charles, 1976).

Edgar, Stuart and John M. Sinton, *The Solway Junction Railway* (Headington, Oxford: Oakwood Press, 1990).

Freeman Fox & Partners, *The Medway Bridge on the M2 Motorway* (London: Cement and Concrete Association, 1962).

Kirwan, Joseph, *A Descriptive and Historical Account of the Liverpool and Manchester Railway, from its First Projection to the Present Time* (Glasgow and London: W. R. M'Phun and Simpkin & Marshall, 1831).

MacDermot, E.T., *History of the Great Western Railway* (London: Great Western Railway Company, 1927).

Maynard, Henry, *Handbook to the Crumlin Viaduct, Monmouthshire [...]* (Crumlin and London: J. M. Wilson and Virtue & Co., 1862, repr. Lydney: Black Dwarf Publications, 2000).

Report of the Court of Inquiry and Report of Mr Rothery Upon the Circumstances Attending the Fall of a portion of the Tay Bridge on the 28th of December, 1879 (London: For Her Majesty's Stationery Office, 1880).

Roscoe, Thomas, *The Book of the Grand Junction Railway* (London: 1839).

Roscoe, Thomas, *The London & Birmingham Railway, with the Home and Country Scenes on Each Side of the Line* (London: Charles Tilt, 1839).

Williams, Frederick S. *The Midland Railway: Its Rise and Progress* (London: Bemrose, 1877).

Biography and Autobiography

Brindle, Steven, *Brunel – The Man Who Changed the World* (London: Weidenfeld & Nicolson, 2005).

Hunter, James Kelso, *Scenes from an Artist's Life* (1868).

Jones, Stephen K., *Brunel in South Wales* (3 vols) (Stroud: History Press 2005 – 2009).

MacKay, Thomas, *The Life of Sir John Fowler, Engineer* (London: John Murray, 1900).

Mitchell, Joseph, *Reminiscences of my life in the Highlands* (2 vols) (1st publ. London: 1883–4; repr. Newton Abbot: David & Charles, 1971).

Owens, Victoria, *James Brindley and the Duke of Bridgewater – Canal Visionaries* (Stroud: Amberley Publishing, 2015).

Rolt, L. T. C., *George and Robert Stephenson* (Pelican, 1960).

Skeat, W. O. *George Stephenson – The Engineer and his Letters* (London: Institution of Mechanical Engineers, 1973).

The Life of Sir William Fairbairn, Bart: Partly Written by Himself, ed. William Pole (London: Longman, Green & Co., 1877; repr. Newton Abbot: David and Charles, 1970).

Yeomans, David and David Cottam, *Owen Williams: The Engineer's Contribution to Contemporary Architecture* (Edinburgh; Edinburgh University, 2001).

General

Burton, Anthony, *The Canal Builders* (Newton Abbot: David & Charles, 1972).

Charlesworth, George, *A History of British Motorways* (London: Thomas Telford Ltd, 1984).

De Maré, Eric, *Bridges of Britain* (London and Sydney: Batsford, 1975).

Ferguson, Hugh and Michael Chrimes, *The Contractors* (London: ICE Publishing, 2014).

Freeman, Michael, *Railways and the Victorian Imagination* (New Haven and London: Yale University Press, 1999).

Lewis, Christopher, *The Canal Pioneers: Brindley's School of Engineers* (Stroud: The History Press: 2011).

McFetrich, David, *An Encyclopaedia of Britain's Bridges* (Kettering: Priory Ash Publishing, 2010).

Repton, Humphry and J. Adey Repton F.A.S., *Fragments on the Theory and Practice of Landscape Gardening* (London: T. Bensley & Son, 1816*)*.

Robbins, Michael, *The Railway Age* (Harmondsworth: Penguin, 1965).

Rolt, L. T. C., *Red for Danger* (David & Charles, 1966).

Rolt, L. T. C., *Victorian Engineering* (Penguin, 1970).

Simmons, Jack and Gordon Biddle, *The Oxford Companion to British Railway History* (Oxford: Oxford University Press, 1997).

Smith, Martin, *British Railway Bridges & Viaducts* (Ian Allan, 1994).

Wolmar, Christian, *Fire and Steam – How the Railways Transformed Britain* (London: Atlantic, 2007).

Index of Bridges and Engineers/Contractors

Aqueducts

Avoncliff 13
Barton 5, 7
Bramwith (Don) 22, 23
Brinklow 6, 8
Cosgrove ('Iron Trunk') 18
Dove 6, 8
Dundas 13
Edstone 18, 19
Engine Arm 20, 21
Kelvin 10, 11, 12
Longdon-on-Tern 15, 16
Lumb Brook 6, 7, 8
Lune 13, 14
Nynehead 19, 21
Pontcyssyllte 15, 17, 18
Rea 10, 11
Stanley Ferry 20, 22
Stourton 6, 7
Teme 9, 10
Tone 19, 20
Vyrnwy 6, 9, 10
Wootton Wawen 18, 19
Yarningale 20

Viaducts

Adam Viaduct, Wigan 86
Advie 85, 86
Ais Gill 63, 67

Alston Arches (Haltwhistle) 41
Armathwaite 72, 73
Arten Gill 63, 64, 65
Aultnaslanach 52, 53
Balcombe 34, 36, 37
Ballochmyle 39
Barmouth 52, 53
Belah 58
Bennerley 58, 59
Calstock 81, 82, 83
Cefn Coed y Cymmer 45, 46
Crosby Garrett 63, 67, 69
Crowdundle 63, 67, 71
Crumlin 56, 57
Dandry Mire 63, 64, 66
Dent 62, 64
Dutton 34, 35
Dry Beck 63, 72, 73
Findhorn (Forres) 47, 48
Findhorn (Tomartin) 58, 59 (Paterson);
    83, 84, 86 (Williams)
Forth Bridge 78, 79
Gaunless 28, 29
Gelt 31
Glenfinnan 81, 82, 83
Goitre Coed 41, 42, 43, 44
Griseburn 63
Hengoed 45, 47
Holmes Chapel 36, 37
Hoo Brook (Kidderminster) 50, 51
Ingleton 61
Killiecrankie 47, 48

Laigh Milton 26, 27
Liskeard 50
Little Salkeld 72
'London–Greenwich Railway or Viaduct'
   32, 33
Long Marton 63, 67, 70
Long Meg 72
Lugar 38
Medway 88
Meldon 58, 59
Moorswater 50, 52
Neath 86, 87, 88
Neidpath 41, 42
Newcastle High Level Bridge 54, 55
Ormside 63, 69, 70
Ouseburn 49
Pease (Cockburnspath) 25
Pont Sarn 45, 46
Ribblehead 62, 63
Risca 25
Roxburgh 38
Royal Border Bridge 36, 38
Saddleworth 40, 41
Sankey 30
Skerne 28, 29
Smardale 62, 67, 68, 72
Solway 74, 75, 76
Stockport 36, 37
Tay Bridge (Bouch) 76, 77
Tay Bridge (Barlows) 77, 78, 79
Thelwall 89, 90
Tilt 47, 48
Torksey 54
Wetheral 31
Wharncliffe 34, 35, 36
Willington Dene 49, 50
Wolverton 42, 43, 44, 45

Engineers/Contractors

Abbott, Samuel 58
Arrol, William 79
Barlow, William Henry and Crawford
   77, 78, 79
Bouch, Thomas 58, 76, 77, 79
Brassey, Thomas 33
Brindley, James 4, 6, 40
Brunel, Isambard 34, 41, 42, 49
Brunel, Marc 6
Brunlees, James 74, 75
Buck, George Watson 6, 36
Christiani & Neilsen 88
Conybeare, Henry 44
Crossley, John Sydney 60, 61, 67, 72
Dadford, Thomas (Senior) 6
Dadford, Thomas (Junior) 6, 9, 10, 11
Dadford, John 6
Fowler, John 54, 77, 79
Freeman Fox & Co. 88
Giles, Francis 28, 31
Green, James 19, 20, 21
Green, John and Benjamin 49, 50
Henderson, David 25
Henshall, Hugh 6, 8
Hodgkinson, John 25
Jee, Alfred Stanistreet 40
Jessop, William 15, 17, 26, 27
Johnson, Richard 58
Kennard, Thomas William 56, 57
Kier, J. L. 88
Landmann, George Thomas 32
Lang, John 81
Leather, George and William 20
Locke, Joseph 33
McAlpine, Robert 81, 82, 83
McIntosh, Hugh 32, 34
Miller, John 36, 38, 39
Mitchell, Joseph 47
Mocatta, David 34, 36
Paterson, Murdoch 52, 53, 58
Raistrick, John Urpeth 34, 36
Rendel, Palmer & Tritton 87
Rennie, John 9, 13, 14
Repton, Humphry 24
Savin, Thomas 44, 45
Stephenson, George 26, 28, 29
Stephenson, Robert 36, 42, 43, 53, 54
Sutherland, Alexander 44, 45
Telford, Thomas 15, 16, 17, 20
Vignoles, Charles 6
Whitmore, William 17, 18
Whitworth, Robert 11
Williams, Owen 83, 84, 86

Acknowledgments

The author and publisher would like to thank the following organisations for permission to use copyright material in this book: The British Library, London; The British Museum, London; The Brunel Institute, Bristol; Head of Steam, Darlington; the University of Bristol Library, Special Collections; and Kidderminster Public Library.

Every attempt has been made to seek permission for copyright material used in this book. However, if we have inadvertently used copyright material without permission/acknowledgment, we apologise and we will make the necessary correction at the first opportunity.

As author, I would like to express my appreciation to Debra Francis at the Institution of Civil Engineers, London; to Michael Richardson, Special Collections Librarian at the University of Bristol; Nick Booth, archivist at the Brunel Institute, Bristol; and to Angela Care at Kidderminster Public Library for their friendly assistance. Connor Stait at Amberley Publishing has been an inspirational editor. I would also like to thank Steve Brewer and Terry Jones for a delightful tour of the viaducts around Merthyr Tydfil; Judith Hibbs, who joined me in walking the route of the 1838 London & Greenwich Railway; Heather Freeman for her superb photography of the Pontcyssyllte Aqueduct; Mike Watkins of the Friends of the Leominster Canal, for details concerning Thomas Dadford's Teme and Rea Aqueducts; Christine Richardson for her wonderful photograph of the Bramwith Aqueduct and information about the River Don and the new Junction Canal; and my husband David for his comments on the text, in addition to inspired map-reading, resourceful parking and companionship on many bridge expeditions.

Between the 1760s and the 1960s, the bridge-stock of Great Britain increased massively, first to accommodate the canal network and later the railway system. It is on this period of prolific aqueduct and viaduct building that my account focusses. Aqueducts and viaducts are both types of bridges, and in this book the word 'bridge' is used interchangeably for both terms.

Victoria Owens
Bristol, 2018